MINOR AND TRACE ELEMENTS
IN BREAST MILK

WITHDRAWN

The World Health Organization is a specialized agency of the United Nations with primary responsibility for international health matters and public health. Through this organization, which was created in 1948, the health professions of some 165 countries exchange their knowledge and experience with the aim of making possible the attainment by all citizens of the world by the year 2000 of a level of health that will permit them to lead a socially and economically productive life.

By means of direct technical cooperation with its Member States, and by stimulating such cooperation among them, WHO promotes the development of comprehensive health services, the prevention and control of diseases, the improvement of environmental conditions, the development of health manpower, the coordination and development of biomedical and health services research, and the planning and implementation of health programmes.

These broad fields of endeavour encompass a wide variety of activities, such as developing systems of primary health care that reach the whole population of Member countries; promoting the health of mothers and children; combating malnutrition; controlling malaria and other communicable diseases including tuberculosis and leprosy; having achieved the eradication of smallpox, promoting mass immunization against a number of other preventable diseases; improving mental health; providing safe water supplies; and training health personnel of all categories.

Progress towards better health throughout the world also demands international cooperation in such matters as establishing international standards for biological substances, pesticides and pharmaceuticals; formulating environmental health criteria; recommending international nonproprietary names for drugs; administering the International Health Regulations; revising the International Classification of Diseases, Injuries, and Causes of Death; and collecting and disseminating health statistical information.

Further information on many aspects of WHO's work is presented in the Organization's publications.

MINOR AND TRACE ELEMENTS IN BREAST MILK

Report of a Joint WHO/IAEA Collaborative Study

WORLD HEALTH ORGANIZATION
GENEVA
1989

ISBN 92 4 156121 1

TYPESET IN INDIA
PRINTED IN ENGLAND
87/7452–Macmillan/Clays–5000

Contents

Preface

This volume completes a series of publications describing a multinational study on breast-feeding which was initiated by the World Health Organization in 1973. Results of the first phase were published in 1981 in a book entitled *Contemporary patterns of breast-feeding (1)*. The second phase of the study, which was concerned specifically with the volume and composition of breast milk, was published in 1985 (2) and contained data on concentrations of protein, non-protein nitrogen, lactose, fat, lactalbumin, lactoferrin, vitamin A, vitamin C, and some pesticides. Results of analyses for minor and trace elements in milk samples collected from the same study groups in Guatemala, Hungary, the Philippines, Sweden and Zaire and from a study group in Nigeria are presented here.

This work deliberately focused on the study of trace elements, since it was considered that there was a lack of reliable data for the concentration of many such elements in human milk. The elements selected for study included all the known essential trace elements, with the exception of silicon, and some important toxic trace elements. Calcium, chlorine, magnesium, phosphorus, potassium and sodium were also included since, like many of the trace elements, they are biologically essential, and their analysis could be carried out by similar means; further, there are important interactions between some of these elements that are potentially of interest. Altogether, therefore, 24 elements were included in this study, namely: antimony, arsenic, cadmium, calcium, chlorine, chromium, cobalt, copper, fluorine, iodine, iron, lead, magnesium, manganese, mercury, molybdenum, nickel, phosphorus, potassium, selenium, sodium, tin, vanadium and zinc.

Published values for most, if not all, of these elements can be found in the scientific literature, and it is therefore legitimate to question why it was necessary to conduct this study at all. The explanation is simply that some of the analyses are extremely difficult to perform properly, and it is only in recent years, and in very few laboratories, that reliable results have begun to be obtained. Consequently, the scientific literature is full of inconsistent data and it is generally impossible to decide *a priori* whether the differences are real (representing biological or geographical variability) or whether they are simply the result of analytical error. The principal aim of this study was, therefore, to obtain reliable data on the quantities of minor and trace elements present in human milk. A second objective was to find out whether the concentrations of these elements varied significantly with the socioeconomic group or geographical origin of the mothers, and indirectly with their nutritional status.

An important requirement in such a programme is the development and use of suitable procedures for analytical quality assurance, the main components of which, as used in this study, comprise: (1) standardized procedures for the collection of samples; (2) the use of a single reference analytical laboratory for each element (thus eliminating interlaboratory systematic errors); and (3) the use of appropriate analytical reference materials (to provide some assurance of the reliability of the results reported by the reference laboratories).

Acknowledgements

The World Health Organization and the International Atomic Energy Agency wish to express their thanks to the investigators listed below, whose untiring efforts made this study possible. Thanks are also due to the national teams in the six participating countries, to the collaborating analytical laboratories in Europe and to the more than 3000 mothers who, together with their families, took part in the study.

National teams

Guatemala
Dr O. Pineda, Dr J. J. Urrutia and Ms B. Garcia, Institute of Nutrition for Central America and Panama (INCAP), Guatemala

Hungary

Principal investigator
Dr I. Öry, Head, Department of Mother, Child, and Youth Care, Ministry of Health, Budapest

Chief collaborators
Dr P. Cholnoky, Head Paediatrician, General Hospital, Szombathely
Dr Ö. Gaál, Department of Food Chemistry, National Institute of Food and Nutrition, Budapest

Clinical work
Dr M. Csaszar, Miss J. Ács, Mrs M. Csiza and Mrs V. Markóczy, Dr E. Dworschák, Dr Anna Gergely, Dr Katalin Linder-Szotyori

Nigeria

Principal investigator
Dr A. Omolulu, College of Medicine, University of Ibadan, Ibadan

Chief collaborators
Dr O. A. Ketiku and Dr I. O. Akinyele, Department of Human Nutrition, University of Ibadan, Ibadan

Philippines

Principal investigator
Dr V. B. Guzman, Department of Community Health, Institute of Public Health, University of the Philippines System, Manila

Biochemical studies
M. P. Macapinlac, Department of Biochemistry, College of Medicine, University of the Philippines System, Manila

Field directors
L. V. del Castillo and T. R. Lariosa, Department of Community Health, Institute of Public Health, University of the Philippines System, Manila

Sweden

Principal investigator
Professor Y. Hofvander, Department of Paediatrics, University Hospital, Uppsala

Clinical work
U. Hagman, The Swedish National Food Administration, Stockholm

Laboratory work
G. Fransson, Professor L. Hambraeus, and L. Wahlberg, Institute of Nutrition, Uppsala University, Uppsala.
H. Jonsson, B. Larsson, C. E. Linder, R. Ras and S. A. Slarach, The Swedish National Food Administration, Stockholm

Zaire

Principal investigator
Professor H. L. Vis, Institute of Scientific Research, Kinshasa; Department of Paediatrics, Free University of Brussels, Brussels, Belgium

Clinical work
P. Hennart, Field Director, Zaire Institute of Scientific Research, Kinshasa, Ruchababisha-Migabo and Nyampeta Uwaytu

Biochemical studies
I. Mandelbaum, Director, Paediatrics Laboratory, St Peter's Hospital, Free University of Brussels, Brussels, Belgium
E. Colombara, P. Devroede, A. Vuye, and N. Herremans, Free University of Brussels, Brussels, Belgium

International Atomic Energy Agency

Principal investigator and study coordinator
R. M. Parr, Department of Research and Isotopes

Laboratory work
R. Ogris, F. Reichel and E. Zeiller

Biostatistics
S. Clements

Analytical laboratories

Finland

Principal investigator
L. Niinistö, Laboratory of Inorganic and Analytical Chemistry, Helsinki University of Technology, Espoo

Federal Republic of Germany, Dortmund

Principal investigator
G. Schöch, Forschungsinstitut für Kinderernährung, Heinstück 11, Dortmund

Laboratory work
V. Galgan

Federal Republic of Germany, Jülich

Principal investigator and analyst
G. V. Iyengar, Institut für Medizin, Kernforschungsanlage Jülich, Jülich

United Kingdom

Principal investigator
G. F. Kirkbright,[a] Department of Instrumentation and Analytical Science, University of Manchester Institute of Science and Technology, Manchester
N. W. Barnett, Department of Environmental Sciences, Plymouth Polytechnic, Plymouth, Devon

---

[a] Now deceased.

Laboratory work
L. S. Chen and M. J. Cope, Department of Instrumentation and Analytical Science, University of Manchester Institute of Science and Technology, Manchester

Yugoslavia

Principal investigator
A. R. Byrne, Nuclear Chemistry Section, "Jozef Stefan" Institute, Ljubljana

Scientific co-workers
M. Dermelj and A. Vakselj

World Health Organization

Dr A. Petros-Barvazian, Division of Family Health, Geneva
Dr A. Pradilla, Nutrition, Division of Family Health, Geneva

Principal investigator and study coordinator
Dr E. M. DeMaeyer, Geneva (*Consultant*)

1. Trace elements in human nutrition

Trace elements have a variety of biochemical functions in all living organisms, and their presence in amounts that are too high or too low can have important consequences.

Among the numerous trace elements, 15 (arsenic, chromium, cobalt, copper, fluorine, iodine, iron, manganese, molybdenum, nickel, selenium, silicon, tin, vanadium and zinc) are currently thought to be essential for humans (though for some of them—arsenic, nickel, tin and vanadium—the only evidence comes from animal experiments).

Historically, the need for iron has been known since the seventeenth century. Similarly, the role of iodine as an essential component of human and animal health was recognized in about 1850. However, most of our knowledge of the remaining essential trace elements was acquired in this century, particularly since 1950. The roles played by these elements are numerous. In some cases they serve as constituents of vital biological molecules (such as iron in haemoglobin and iodine in thyroid hormones); in others they are either part of an enzyme system or exert their influence as co-factors for various reactions mediated by enzymes. Table 1 summarizes the biochemical roles and signs of deficiency in humans of the 15 essential trace elements.

Trace elements are known to play a particularly important role in growth and development. In animals, it has been demonstrated through extensive experiments that there is a need for an adequate supply of essential trace elements, such as copper, iron, manganese and zinc, for growth and development of the neonate (3, 4). Deficiencies of these elements may result in poor growth, abnormal overall development, skin disorders, bone fractures and increased neonatal morbidity. In human subjects, copper, selenium and zinc deficiency syndromes have been reported during the last 20 years (5, 6).

The young of all species are specially susceptible to the effects of trace element deficiencies. For example, iron deficiency impairs intellectual development in young children, and iodine deficiency has serious effects, both before and after birth, on mental development and physical growth. Similarly, serious growth retardation results

1

Table 1. Classification of essential trace elements

Element	Year of discovery of element's importance	Function	Deficiency signs in humans
Iron	17th century	Oxygen, electron transport	Anaemia
Iodine	1850	Constituent of thyroid hormones	Goitre, depression of thyroid function, cretinism
Copper	1928	Constituent of oxidative enzymes; interaction with iron; cross-linking of elastin	Anaemia, changes of ossification, possibly elevated serum cholesterol
Manganese	1931	Mucopolysaccharide metabolism; constituent of superoxide dismutase	Not known
Zinc	1934	Constituent of numerous enzymes involved in energy metabolism and in transcription and translation	Growth depression, sexual immaturity, skin lesions, depression of immunocompetence, change of taste acuity
Cobalt	1935	Constituent of vitamin B_{12}	Only as vitamin B_{12} deficiency
Molybdenum	1953	Constituent of xanthine, aldehyde and sulfide oxidases	Not known
Selenium	1957	Constituent of glutathione peroxidase; interaction with heavy metals	Endemic cardiomyopathy (Keshan disease) caused by selenium deficiency
Chromium	1959	Potentiation of insulin	Relative insulin resistance, impaired glucose tolerance, elevated serum lipids
Tin	1970	Not known	Not known
Vanadium	1971	Not known	Not known
Fluorine	1971	Structure of teeth, possibly of bones; possible growth effect	Increased incidence of caries, possible risk factor for osteoporosis
Silicon	1972	Calcification possible function in connective tissue	Not known
Nickel	1976	Interaction with iron absorption	Not known
Arsenic	1977	Not known	Not known

from zinc deficiency in infants and children, while adolescents may suffer from delayed sexual maturation.

In this context, infant nutrition, especially during the early stages of infancy, assumes special importance. Human milk, or a simulated version of it such as a milk formula product, is usually the only source of food for infants during the first months of life. It is therefore essential that it should contain all necessary nutrients in adequate amounts. This is particularly important for elements that are not stored by the fetus *in utero*. From this point of view one can distinguish two groups of elements: those such as copper and iron for which body stores are normally sufficient at birth to protect the infant from deficiency for 4–6 months, and those such as selenium and zinc, for which body stores are not extensive and which therefore need to be taken in sufficient quantities at all times to maintain optimal growth and development.

Spurred on by this kind of knowledge, many governments have started to specify recommended dietary intakes of minor and trace elements. Supplementation of human diets in general, and of infant diets in particular, with elements such as iron, iodine, and fluorine is already being promoted by national health authorities, and in at least one country (Finland) indirect supplementation with selenium (via fertilizer applied to farmland) has recently been started.

As far as infant foods are concerned, the main issue is whether milk formula products consumed by babies who are not breast-fed contain adequate levels of essential nutrients. A WHO Expert Committee report in 1973 (7) contained recommendations for levels of essential trace elements in milk formula, based on the levels found in human or cow's milk but noted that there was a need for additional information on the quantities of trace elements present in human milk if the recommendations were to be implemented successfully. This, therefore, was the principal aim of the study described in this report.

2. Methods

Sample collection

As outlined in the report on the second phase of this study (2), three groups of mothers were studied in each of the six countries participating in this project:

— urban well-to-do or economically advantaged mothers (group 1);
— urban poor or economically disadvantaged mothers (group 2); and
— rural mothers following a traditional way of life in families mostly dependent on subsistence agriculture and local marketing. (group 3).

The centres collaborating in the project were located in Guatemala, Hungary, Nigeria, the Philippines, Sweden, and Zaire. It was realized that, in some of these countries, the groupings indicated above would have little meaning, and therefore modifications to this general scheme were agreed in advance. The communities from which the mothers were selected and the characteristics of the study samples were described in detail in the report on the second phase (2). The groups studied in each of the countries, together with the number of human milk specimens provided for analysis, are specified in Table 2.

It was decided to study the composition of human milk at about three months after the birth of the baby. At this stage of lactation the milk is relatively mature and many of its constituents have reached fairly stable levels. Moreover, three months is the time at which many mothers start to wean their babies. After this age, therefore, the baby's intake of nutrients no longer depends exclusively on breast milk.

One of the important practical problems in this kind of research is that many of the elements of interest are present at such low levels that contamination of the samples by the use of impure or inadequately cleaned equipment can seriously affect the results. Specially prepared and cleaned collection vessels and specimen vials were therefore supplied to all collection centres. A special detergent (baby shampoo) containing low levels of trace elements was also supplied for washing the breast prior to the collection of the milk.

Details of the sample collection and reporting procedures are given in Annexes 1 and 2. For the analysis of the minor and trace elements by the reference analytical laboratories, samples of 20–30 ml of milk were requested. Some of the collection centres retained an additional

4

Table 2. Information on the areas and groups included in the study and the number of human milk specimens provided for analysis

| Study area | Study group | | No. of specimens |
	Code	Description	
Guatemala	1	Well-to-do mothers	31
	2	Urban poor mothers	29
	3	Mothers living in a rural environment	40
Hungary	1	Mothers with university education	24
	2	Mothers with primary education	33
	3	Mothers living in a rural environment	25
Nigeria	1	Well-to-do mothers	6
	2	Urban poor mothers	2
	3	Mothers living in a rural environment	10
Philippines	1	Well-to-do mothers	46
	2	Urban poor mothers	74
	3	Mothers living in a rural environment	63
Sweden	All	One group of mothers (urban and rural)	64
Zaire	1	Urban mothers[a]	37
	3	Rural mothers	32

[a] The distinction between very poor and not-so-poor urban mothers was thought to be impracticable.

aliquot for their own analyses. All the specimens were collected by specially trained personnel who kept records of relevant data on each mother and her child.

After a sufficient number of samples had been collected, they were shipped to the IAEA laboratory in Vienna, Austria in low-temperature transport containers which kept them frozen at $-11°C$ during shipment.

Analysis

It was recognized that there is probably no laboratory in existence that has the ideal combination of facilities and expertise required for analysing reliably all 24 of the elements identified as being of interest in this study. For this reason the workload was shared among a group of experienced analytical laboratories employing a variety of analytical methods. Table 3 lists the laboratories involved and the methods employed. Further details of the latter are given in Annexes 3–9.

One feature of the experimental design was that each element was analysed by only one reference laboratory, thus avoiding the problem of interlaboratory differences. The quality of the data reported by each laboratory was checked by means of two milk-based standard

Table 3. Reference analytical laboratories, elements determined, and analytical methods

Analytical laboratory	Elements determined	Analytical method	Annex[a]
IAEA, Vienna, Austria	Ca, Cr, K, Mg, Na	Atomic absorption spectrometry	3
	Cl	Instrumental NAA[b]	4
	Cd, Mo	Radiochemical NAA	4
Kernforschungsanlage (KFA), Jülich, Federal Republic of Germany	Co, Fe, Hg, Sb, Se, Zn	Instrumental NAA	5
	Cu, Mn	Radiochemical NAA	5
Institute of Science and Technology, Manchester, United Kingdom	Ni	Emission spectrometry (ICP-OES[b])	6
	Pb	Atomic absorption spectrometry	6
Jozef Stefan Institute, Ljubljana, Yugoslavia	As, I, Sn, Vd	Radiochemical NAA	7
Helsinki University of Technology, Helsinki, Finland	F	Electrochemistry (ion-specific electrode)	8
Forschungsinstitut für Kinderernährung, Dortmund, Federal Republic of Germany	P	Light absorption spectrometry	9

[a] Further information on methods and analytical quality assurance is provided in this Annex.
[b] NAA, neutron activation analysis; ICP-OES, inductively coupled plasma optical emission spectrometry.

quality control materials, as described on page 8, and by blind analyses of reference materials.

Several of the collection centres carried out their own analyses on duplicate aliquots of some of the samples they had collected. Most of these measurements were made by atomic absorption spectroscopy. The details are not recorded here, but are available on request from the responsible project officers (see Acknowledgements, pages ix–xii).

The IAEA laboratory in Vienna served as a central coordinating laboratory for the analyses. Specimens received from the collection centres were stored at low temperature (approximately −20 °C) until the analyses could be started. After thawing, the vial was placed in an ultrasonic water bath for about five minutes to rehomogenize the sample (see Annex 1). If sufficient material was available (more than 30 ml), six separate aliquots of 5 ml were removed for subsequent analysis by the different reference analysts. However, if, as was often the case, the amount of material provided for analysis was less than 30 ml, then smaller and/or fewer aliquots were prepared. The aliquots were placed in individual precleaned plastic vials, these operations being carried out on a clean-air workbench (using a laminar-flow hood).

Aliquots intended for the determination of calcium, chromium, magnesium, potassium and sodium were refrozen pending analysis; the remaining aliquots were freeze-dried and, after a sufficient number had been collected, were shipped to the appropriate laboratory for analysis.

In cases where insufficient material was available for the preparation of aliquots for each reference analyst, care was taken to distribute the aliquots in such a way that each analyst received a representative selection of specimens from each study group. In general, the analysts were required to analyse each specimen separately. If, however, the amount of material provided was insufficient for an analysis, they were permitted to pool individual specimens according to an agreed set of guidelines (see Annex 2).

Analytical quality assurance

Despite many important advances during the last 20 years in the methodologies available for the determination of trace elements in biological materials, such analyses are still very commonly subject to significant errors, which may be as large as one or more orders of magnitude (8). The difficulties increase the lower the concentrations involved, and in this respect milk is one of the most difficult matrices to study. As noted in Annex 5, uncertainties exist even for the measurement of such commonly studied trace elements as copper.

Since these difficulties had been recognized even before the planning stage of this project, it was decided that considerable attention should be paid from the outset to the development and application of suitable analytical quality assurance procedures. These efforts appear to have been successful for most of the elements of interest, though some residual doubts persist as to the reliability of the data for antimony, cadmium, lead, mercury, nickel, tin and vanadium.

One of the most important components of a quality assurance programme is strict adherence to a suitable protocol for sampling and sample collection. The relevant protocols (Annexes 1 and 2) were developed with this aim in view and, as already noted, collection vessels and specimen vials were precleaned and supplied from a central laboratory. In the absence of any evidence to the contrary, it is assumed that the protocols were followed conscientiously at each of the collection centres. However, it was not feasible to obtain independent confirmation of this.

Another important component of quality assurance in this programme was that a given element was determined in all of the samples and control materials by the same analyst using the same method. This alone, of course, does not guarantee that the analytical methods were all providing reliable data. Evidence on the latter point was obtained using two types of milk-based standards issued by the IAEA and by blind analyses of reference materials.

The first of these was a milk powder certified reference material, code A-11, prepared from cow's milk (9). When this study was started, this was the only such milk-based reference material in existence, though since then several other similar reference materials have become available (10). It has to be recognized, however, that A-11 was far from being an ideal reference standard, since recommended concentrations were not available for all of the elements of interest (see Annex 10), and even for those elements for which recommended[a] concentrations were provided, there is still some uncertainty as to the correctness of some of the values quoted (e.g., for copper, see Annex 5). A-11 is also unsuitable in the sense that cow's milk and human milk differ significantly in the concentrations of some elements. In particular, there is almost a tenfold difference in phosphorus concentration, which is important since this element causes serious interference in the determination of the some of the other elements.

Partly for this reason, but also because of the desirability of a second standard for internal quality control (to monitor the constancy of performance of the analytical methods during the full programme of analysis), an additional reference material was developed based on

---

[a] Recommended concentrations are best estimates of the concentrations of the elements of interest based on the results of interlaboratory testings, technical judgements and statistical analysis. For further information see: PARR, R. ET AL. Survey and evaluation of available biological reference materials for trace element analysis. *Fresenius Zeitung zur analytische Chemie,* **326**: 601–608 (1987).

human milk. It was prepared from a 2-litre pooled specimen of human milk from Hungarian donors. After careful mixing, individual 5-ml aliquots were dispensed into precleaned plastic vials and freeze-dried. These specimens were given the code HM-1.

Throughout the programme, roughly 15% of the total workload comprised analysis of a number of aliquots of A-11 and HM-1. Some of the latter were included in the sample series designated as real samples. The identities of these test aliquots were revealed to the reference analysts only after the completion of the laboratory work. In addition to the two milk-based standards, other certified reference materials such as NBS bovine liver and Bowen's Kale were also used by some analysts to evaluate their methodologies.

The results obtained with these various reference materials are presented in Annexes 3–9. A summary of results for the two milk-based reference materials, A-11 and HM-1, is presented in Annex 10. Further details have been published by Iyengar & Parr (*11*).

Data reporting and evaluation

All analytical data for minor and trace elements were reported to IAEA for evaluation. A report form was used which, in addition to including a sample identification code, the name of the element and the analytical result, also contained other details such as the age of the child and the year and month of sample collection. For further information, see Annexes 1 and 2.

These data were entered into a computer data base and evaluated using standard methods. Since many of the sets of data under consideration did not conform to a simple Gaussian distribution, it was decided to use a method of data evaluation that is relatively insensitive to the exact form of the statistical distribution and to the presence of outliers (*12*). The method chosen was based on the use of the median and its standard deviation, s, as given by the relation:

$$s = \frac{0.926R}{\sqrt{N}}$$

where R is the interquartile range (the difference between the 75th and 25th percentiles) and N is the number of observations.

In Chapter 3, the values of the above-mentioned parameters are presented for each element in tabular form together with the minimum and maximum values in each data set and the 10th, 16th, 84th, and 90th percentiles. (The 16th and 84th percentiles correspond, for a normal Gaussian distribution, to the range: mean $\pm$ standard deviation (SD)). The same data are also represented graphically by so-called "box plots" as shown in the example on page 10. Box plots illustrate the maximum, 75th percentile, median, 25th percentile, and minimum.

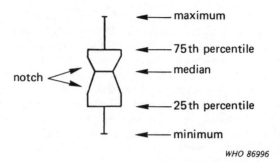

WHO 86996

Note: the width of the box is proportional to $\sqrt{N}$

The size of the notch is represented by the range: median $\pm 1.7\ s$. The advantage of plotting the notch in this way is that it enables the reader to see at a glance whether two sets of data differ significantly from each other. If the respective notches overlap, then the data do not differ significantly, whereas if the notches do not overlap then the data differ significantly at the probability level of 95% (or more if there is a large separation of the notches).

Also included in the tables and plots are comparative data for human milk taken from the scientific literature as reported in a review (*13*). For each literature source, a single value is used for each element (generally the mean, but if this was not available, then the midpoint of the total range).

Several collection centres also analysed some of their own samples for some elements. In cases where such data were made available to IAEA, they are recorded in the relevant tables in Chapter 3 or mentioned in the accompanying text. However, the conclusions of this report are based mainly on the data provided by the reference analytical laboratories.

The data have also been examined for significant differences in respect of samples collected in any one study area: (1) 'from different study groups; and (2) at different times of the year (the year being divided into four trimesters, January to March, April to June, etc.). The same method of evaluation was used (i.e., by means of box plots), although the respective plots are not reproduced here. However, in cases where significant differences were found, this fact is recorded in the relevant parts of Chapter 3 under the subheadings "Other significant findings".

3. Results

In this Chapter, the results obtained are presented on an element-by-element basis in alphabetical order. Where appropriate, remarks are also made on the analytical significance of the results, and on differences between study areas and study groups. The biological significance of these findings is discussed in Chapter 4. Results for individual elements are preceded by a section on total dry matter.

Total dry matter

Although the determination of dry matter was not foreseen as one of the purposes of this project, all specimens received by the central coordinating laboratory were freeze-dried as part of the process of preparing them for subsequent analysis. A statistical summary of the amounts of dry matter. found is presented in Table 4 and, as box plots, in Fig. 1.[a]

Differences between study areas

Several significant differences between study areas were observed, though they were not of very large magnitude in strictly numerical terms. The values for Sweden were relatively high and those for Nigeria relatively low. These observations add further weight to the findings reported in the second phase of the study (2), that the energy content of breast milk of Swedish mothers was significantly higher than that of any other group of mothers.

Differences between study groups within study areas

In Guatemala, values for the rural group were significantly lower than for either of the urban groups; in Zaire, on the other hand, the values for the rural group were higher than those for the urban group. Otherwise no significant differences were observed. These observations are slightly different from the findings reported in the second phase of the study (2) in which no statistically significant differences in energy content were observed between the various study groups.

---

[a] For an explanation of the use of box plots in their various forms see: McGILL, R. ET AL. Variations of box plots. *The American statistician*, **32**: 12–16 (1978).

Table 4. Statistical summary of amounts of dry matter in human milk (g/l original milk); all data from IAEA, Vienna

Study area	Study group	No. of observations	Minimum	Percentiles							Maximum	SD (median)	
				10	16	25	50 median	75	84	90		absolute	relative (%)
Guatemala	1	31	102	108	110	111	116	120	122	125	135	1	1.3
	2	29	99	107	111	114	123	137	144	150	192	4	3.1
	3	40	91	95	97	100	105	117	121	123	128	2	2.4
	All	100	91	100	101	106	115	122	127	135	192	1	1.3
Hungary	1	24	94	107	109	119	126	144	148	157	188	5	3.7
	2	33	96	100	106	112	126	138	146	153	160	4	3.3
	3	25	89	96	105	115	126	134	142	157	170	4	2.8
	All	82	89	102	107	115	126	139	146	151	188	2	1.9
Nigeria	1	6	80	80	82	94	110	126	127	127	127	12	11.0
	2	2	86	86	86	86	95	104	104	104	104	12	12.4
	3	10	54	57	75	96	111	118	120	122	122	6	5.7
	All	18	54	77	81	96	108	118	122	126	127	5	4.5
Philippines	1	46	87	99	105	111	121	126	132	139	153	2	1.7
	2	74	91	98	100	109	117	124	128	131	152	2	1.4
	3	63	75	97	103	108	119	124	134	144	149	2	1.6
	All	183	75	98	103	108	119	124	129	137	153	1	0.9
Sweden	All	64	93	112	114	116	128	137	140	144	162	2	1.9
Zaire	1	37	89	102	106	110	118	126	135	138	143	3	2.1
	3	32	98	104	110	119	128	134	142	145	156	2	1.9
	All	69	89	102	107	113	123	131	138	141	156	2	1.6

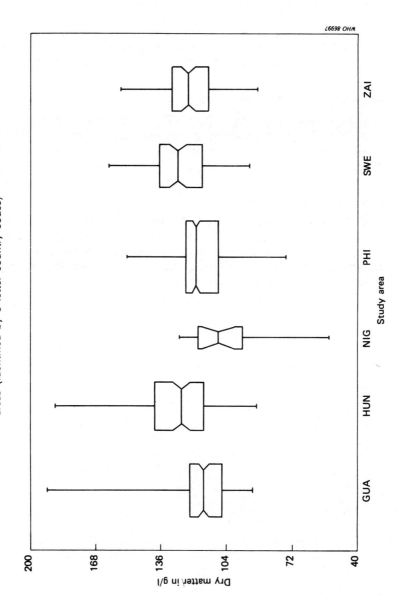

Fig. 1. Box plots showing amounts of dry matter (g/l original milk) in human milk specimens from six study areas (identified by 3-letter country codes)

Antimony

Instrumental neutron activation analysis was used as the reference analytical method for antimony (see Annex 5). Although there are no *a priori* reasons for doubting the reliability of the analytical data, some quality assurance problems were encountered, and further independent confirmation of the accuracy of the analyses would be desirable. The results obtained are presented in Table 5 and Fig. 2.

Differences between study areas

Several very highly significant differences were apparent in the data. The Philippine values were very high; those for Guatemala and Hungary, on the other hand, were relatively low. The data for Nigeria were highly variable.

Other significant findings

In Hungary, samples collected during the third trimester (July–September) contained significantly lower antimony concentrations than those collected at other times of the year. In Sweden, samples collected during the fourth trimester contained significantly higher concentrations than those collected at other times of the year.

Table 5. Statistical summary of amounts of antimony found in human milk (µg/l original milk)

Study area	Study group	No. of observations	Minimum[a]	Percentiles							Maximum	SD (median)	
				10	16	25	50 median	75	84	90		absolute	relative (%)
Data from reference analytical laboratory													
Guatemala	1	21	0.0	0.0	0.3	0.6	0.9	1.4	1.7	1.9	4.3	0.2	18
	2	24	0.0	0.2	0.4	0.6	1.3	2.3	2.5	7.8	10.3	0.3	25
	3	39	0.0	0.0	0.0	0.0	1.0	1.4	1.9	3.2	13.3	0.2	21
	All	84	0.0	0.0	0.0	0.5	1.0	1.6	2.2	2.9	13.3	0.1	11
Hungary	1	21	0.7	0.7	0.8	1.1	1.8	2.4	2.7	3.5	4.0	0.3	16
	2	29	0.2	0.4	0.6	1.0	1.4	2.2	2.6	2.8	7.5	0.2	15
	3	21	0.0	0.0	0.6	0.8	1.3	3.3	4.7	5.9	7.7	0.5	40
	All	71	0.0	0.6	0.7	1.0	1.6	2.3	2.8	3.9	7.7	0.2	10
Nigeria	1	6	0.4	0.4	0.4	0.6	3.2	15.7	17.4	17.7	17.7	5.7	178
	2	2	4.3	4.3	4.3	4.3	7.6	10.9	10.9	10.9	10.9	4.3	57
	3	10	0.2	0.3	0.9	1.5	3.3	10.9	17.5	17.6	17.6	2.8	82
	All	18	0.2	0.4	0.7	1.1	4.1	11.9	17.4	17.6	17.7	2.4	57
Philippines	1	16	3.4	3.4	4.5	6.7	10.7	18.7	24.0	29.9	31.8	2.8	26
	2	28	0.0	2.3	4.4	6.0	12.7	20.5	27.4	34.1	43.0	2.5	20
	3	21	0.0	2.1	3.1	4.3	9.6	16.3	19.8	22.0	38.4	2.4	25
	All	65	0.0	3.0	4.3	5.3	11.0	18.6	22.2	29.5	43.0	1.5	14
Sweden	All	32	0.3	1.2	1.4	2.1	3.0	6.7	8.5	9.3	22.9	0.8	25
Zaire	1	37	0.8	1.2	1.6	2.1	3.5	5.2	6.6	8.4	11.7	0.5	14
	3	32	0.0	1.2	1.9	2.9	3.9	7.5	8.6	13.4	26.6	0.8	19
	All	69	0.0	1.3	1.7	2.2	3.6	5.5	8.1	9.2	26.6	0.4	10
Data from the literature													
	All	1	2.7	2.7	2.7	2.7	2.7	2.7	2.7	2.7	2.7	0.0	0

[a] Zeros indicate values below the detection limit (~0.2 µg/l)

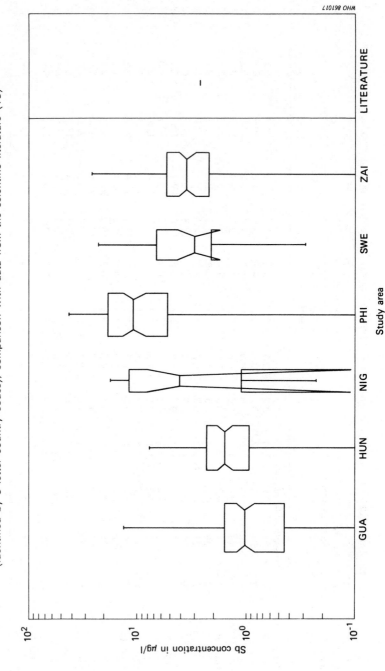

Fig. 2. Box plots showing amounts of antimony (Sb) (µg/l original milk) in human milk specimens from six study areas (identified by 3-letter country codes); comparison with data from the scientific literature (13)

Arsenic

Neutron activation analysis was used as the reference analytical method for arsenic (see Annex 7). Despite the fact that this is a difficult element to measure reliably at the concentrations found in human and animal milk, and that no entirely appropriate certified reference materials were available, there are reasonable grounds for confidence in the analytical method used in this study. The results obtained are presented in Table 6 and Fig. 3.

Differences between study areas

Arsenic concentrations in specimens from the Philippines were considerably higher than those from all other study areas (by more than one order of magnitude). Although the median values for other countries were mostly in the range 0.1–0.6 $\mu g/l$, there were some significant differences (Sweden and Hungary). The Nigerian data had a relatively high median value and a very wide total range.

Other significant findings

In Guatemala, milk samples collected between October and December had significantly lower arsenic concentrations than those collected from January to March.

Table 6. Statistical summary of amounts of arsenic found in human milk (μg/l original milk)

Study area	Study group	No. of obser-vations	Minimum	Percentiles							Maximum	SD (median)	
				10	16	25	50 median	75	84	90		absolute	relative (%)
Data from reference analytical laboratory													
Guatemala	1	8	0.08	0.08	0.09	0.13	0.45	0.64	1.73	2.57	2.57	0.17	38
	2	8	0.23	0.23	0.25	0.28	0.38	0.72	0.86	0.93	0.93	0.15	38
	3	10	0.09	0.09	0.10	0.11	0.12	0.28	0.37	0.50	0.52	0.05	41
	All	26	0.08	0.10	0.11	0.11	0.29	0.53	0.64	0.82	2.57	0.08	26
Hungary	1	4	0.21	0.21	0.21	0.22	0.26	1.17	1.47	1.47	1.47	0.44	170
	2	4	0.11	0.11	0.11	0.13	0.20	0.24	0.25	0.25	0.25	0.05	25
	3	3	0.24	0.24	0.24	0.24	0.28	0.31	0.31	0.31	0.31	0.03	13
	All	11	0.11	0.12	0.19	0.20	0.24	0.28	0.40	1.24	1.47	0.02	8
Nigeria	1	1	1.10	1.10	1.10	1.10	1.10	1.10	1.10	1.10	1.10	0.00	0
	2	1	0.59	0.59	0.59	0.59	0.59	0.59	0.59	0.59	0.59	0.00	0
	3	4	0.83	0.83	0.83	1.23	2.59	8.26	10.10	10.10	10.10	3.25	126
	All	6	0.59	0.59	0.62	0.77	1.78	4.57	9.22	10.10	10.10	1.44	81
Philippines	1	3	8.35	8.35	8.35	8.35	14.17	18.40	18.40	18.40	18.40	5.37	38
	2	5	1.13	1.13	1.13	4.42	12.46	25.81	32.25	32.25	32.25	8.86	71
	3	6	17.56	17.56	18.22	21.71	26.17	47.04	87.81	95.57	95.57	9.57	37
	All	14	1.13	4.42	7.97	11.43	18.89	27.57	31.69	63.91	95.57	3.99	21
Sweden	All	8	0.37	0.37	0.37	0.41	0.55	0.87	3.49	5.49	5.49	0.15	27
Zaire	1	10	0.13	0.13	0.16	0.18	0.22	0.39	0.43	0.49	0.50	0.06	27
	3	10	0.14	0.14	0.14	0.15	0.46	0.62	0.72	0.80	0.82	0.14	30
	All	20	0.13	0.14	0.15	0.17	0.26	0.54	0.59	0.69	0.82	0.08	29
Data from the literature													
	All	2	3.20	3.20	3.20	3.20	19.60	36.00	36.00	36.00	36.00	21.48	110

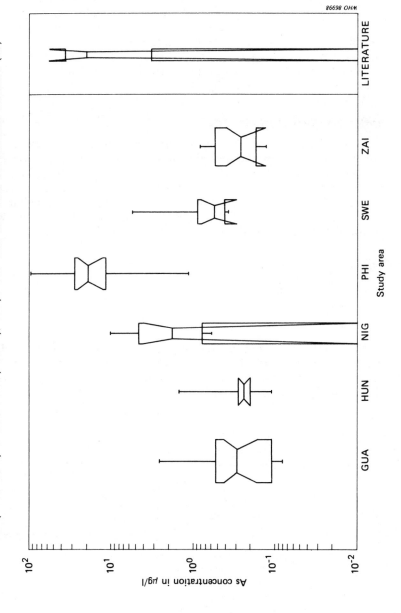

Fig. 3. Box plots showing amounts of arsenic (As) (μg/l original milk) in human milk specimens from six study areas (identified by 3-letter country codes); comparison with data from the scientific literature (13)

Cadmium

Neutron activation analysis was used as the reference analytical method for cadmium (see Annex 4). Measurements of various quality control materials confirmed that, as far as could be judged, this method was accurate. However, many of the milk samples contained cadmium at levels close to, or below, the limit of detection. For this reason it was not always possible to obtain meaningful values for the medians and other statistical parameters. The results obtained are presented in Table 7 and Fig. 4.

Differences betwen study areas

Although most of the milk samples contained cadmium at concentrations below the detection limit of the method, the available data nevertheless show that specimens from the Philippines had significantly higher levels than those from most other collection centres. The Nigerian data also had a high median value but the range was very large. All the values for specimens from Zaire were below the detection limit.

Other significant findings

There were none.

Other data

Two of the collection centres engaged in this study provided data: Sweden and Hungary. Their values were consistent with those from the reference laboratory, bearing in mind that the latter reported a detection limit of about 1 μg/1.

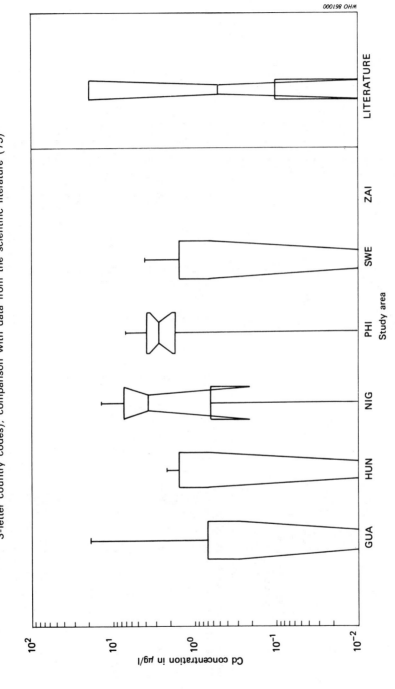

Fig. 4. Box plots showing amounts of cadmium (Cd) (μg/l original milk) in human milk specimens from six study areas (identified by 3-letter country codes); comparison with data from the scientific literature (13)

Table 7. Statistical summary of amounts of cadmium in human milk (μg/l original milk)[a]

Study area	Study group	No. of obser-vations	Minimum	Percentiles							Maximum	SD (median)	
				10	16	25	50 median	75	84	90		absolute	relative (%)
Data from reference analytical laboratory													
Guatemala	1	3	0.00	0.00	0.00	0.00	0.00	18.63	18.63	18.63	18.63	9.96	
	2	2	0.00	0.00	0.00	0.00	0.00	0.00	0.00	0.00	0.00	0.00	
	3	8	0.00	0.00	0.00	0.00	0.00	1.03	1.78	2.10	2.10	0.34	
	All	13	0.00	0.00	0.00	0.00	0.00	0.69	1.93	12.02	18.63	0.18	
Hungary	1	3	0.00	0.00	0.00	0.00	0.00	0.00	0.00	0.00	0.00	0.00	
	2	5	0.00	0.00	0.00	0.00	0.00	1.65	1.76	1.76	1.76	0.68	
	3	3	0.00	0.00	0.00	0.00	0.00	2.17	2.17	2.17	2.17	1.16	
	All	11	0.00	0.00	0.00	0.00	0.00	1.54	1.80	2.09	2.17	0.43	
Nigeria	1	4	1.26	1.26	1.26	1.86	6.07	12.44	13.77	13.77	13.77	4.90	81
	2	2	2.60	2.60	2.60	2.60	4.29	5.98	5.98	5.98	5.98	2.21	52
	3	3	0.00	0.00	0.00	0.00	0.00	4.15	4.15	4.15	4.15	2.22	
	All	9	0.00	0.00	0.00	0.63	3.67	7.22	10.58	13.77	13.77	2.03	55
Philippines	1	5	1.69	1.69	1.69	1.94	2.67	3.67	4.06	4.06	4.06	0.72	27
	2	6	0.00	0.00	0.00	0.00	2.06	3.10	4.15	4.35	4.35	1.17	57
	3	4	1.50	1.50	1.50	1.86	3.35	6.12	6.90	6.90	6.90	1.97	59
	All	15	0.00	0.00	0.84	1.69	2.67	3.77	4.19	5.37	6.90	0.50	19
Sweden	All	13	0.00	0.00	0.00	0.00	0.00	1.51	2.50	3.46	4.03	0.39	
Zaire	1	7	0.00	0.00	0.00	0.00	0.00	0.00	0.00	0.00	0.00	0.00	
	3	8	0.00	0.00	0.00	0.00	0.00	0.00	0.00	0.00	0.00	0.00	
	All	15	0.00	0.00	0.00	0.00	0.00	0.00	0.00	0.00	0.00	0.00	

Data from collection centres (for their own samples)

		n										
Hungary	1	1	0.50	0.50	0.50	0.50	0.50	0.50	0.50	0.50	0.00	0
	2	1	0.50	0.50	0.50	0.50	0.50	0.50	0.50	0.50	0.00	0
	3	3	0.60	0.60	0.60	0.60	0.60	0.60	0.60	0.60	0.00	0
	All		0.50	0.50	0.50	0.50	0.60	0.60	0.60	0.60	0.05	11
Sweden	All	39	0.10	0.10	0.10	0.10	0.20	0.20	0.40	3.80	0.01	15

Data from the literature

		n										
	All	3	0.10	0.10	0.10	0.50	19.00	19.00	19.00	19.00	10.10	2000

[a] Zeros indicate values below the detection limit ($\sim$1 µg/l) (see Annex 4).

Calcium

Flame atomic absorption spectrometry was used as the reference analytical method for calcium (see Annex 3). The quality assurance data obtained during the course of the project confirmed that this method had satisfactory accuracy and precision. The results obtained are presented in Table 8 and Fig. 5.

Differences between study areas

Most of the concentrations reported were in the range 200–300 mg/1. Guatemala had significantly higher values than most other study areas, though the differences were not very large. The Nigerian and Swedish values were slightly lower than those for most other study areas.

Other significant findings

In Guatemala, the three study groups differed significantly from each other (urban elite > rural > urban poor). There were no significant differences in the other study areas.

Other data

Four collection centres provided data: Hungary, the Philippines, and Sweden (see Table 8), and Zaire (urban, 248 ± 23 mg/1;[a] rural, 288 ± 11 mg/l[a]). Satisfactory agreement with the results from the reference laboratory was observed except for those from the Philippines, which were significantly lower. It is assumed that the reasons for this discrepancy were analytical.

---

[a] Mean $\pm$ SD for specimens collected 3 months after birth.

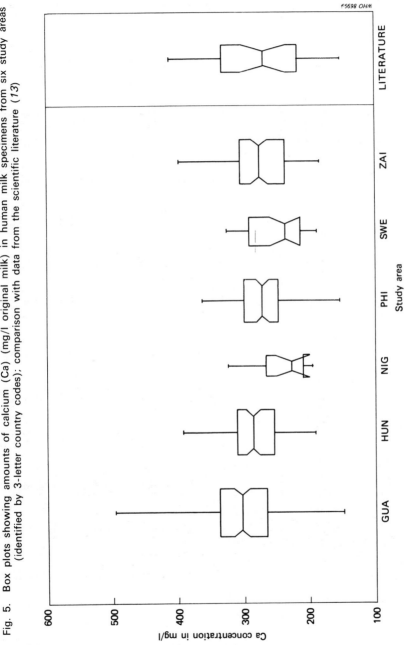

Fig. 5. Box plots showing amounts of calcium (Ca) (mg/l original milk) in human milk specimens from six study areas (identified by 3-letter country codes); comparison with data from the scientific literature (13)

Table 8. Statistical summary of amounts of calcium found in human milk (mg/l original milk)

Study area	Study group	No. of obser- vations	Minimum	Percentiles							Maximum	SD (median)	
				10	16	25	50 median	75	84	90		absolute	relative (%)
Data from reference analytical laboratory													
Guatemala	1	22	257	264	282	306	346	381	407	417	496	15	4
	2	22	147	209	215	221	263	297	327	355	417	15	6
	3	37	246	253	265	278	303	322	339	359	382	7	2
	All	81	147	238	251	265	303	337	359	376	496	7	2
Hungary	1	21	226	236	246	252	287	311	328	351	366	12	4
	2	29	245	251	252	260	281	317	324	339	391	10	3
	3	21	190	227	243	246	277	307	324	342	373	12	4
	All	71	190	244	250	253	285	310	320	340	391	6	2
Nigeria	1	5	204	204	204	213	226	281	323	323	323	28	12
	2	1	194	194	194	194	194	194	194	194	194	0	0
	3	9	203	203	206	209	236	274	284	286	286	20	9
	All	15	194	199	204	208	226	265	284	301	323	14	6
Philippines	1	16	207	208	222	247	268	317	332	342	345	16	6
	2	28	179	201	222	247	283	304	320	330	362	10	4
	3	21	152	194	218	233	265	289	298	328	342	11	4
	All	65	152	208	219	246	270	299	320	331	362	6	2
Sweden	All	29	187	199	203	212	235	290	292	295	324	13	6
Zaire	1	37	182	221	231	241	284	307	314	319	359	10	4
	3	32	205	215	228	234	261	294	323	333	396	10	4
	All	69	182	223	229	235	274	304	317	324	396	8	3

Data from collection centres (for their own samples)

Hungary	1	19	204	208	217	250	334	392	400	428	460	30	9
	2	31	210	234	242	254	286	352	398	419	432	16	6
	3	22	200	237	247	254	285	361	434	511	580	21	7
	All	72	200	224	241	254	288	376	400	425	580	13	5
Philippines	1	19	171	171	180	188	221	255	271	280	304	14	6
	2	29	171	175	186	205	238	255	262	272	290	9	4
	3	27	128	159	188	205	221	248	265	274	280	8	3
	All	75	128	173	188	205	221	254	265	272	304	5	2
Sweden	All	28	195	216	221	229	250	288	302	303	318	10	4

Data from the literature

	All	27	150	167	177	215	267	330	336	345	410	20	8

Chlorine

Neutron activation analysis was used as the reference analytical method for chlorine (see Annex 4). The quality assurance data obtained during the course of the project confirmed that this method was working with satisfactory accuracy and precision. The results obtained are presented in Table 9 and Fig. 6.

Differences between study areas

Most study areas had similar median values of around 300–400 mg/l. There were no significant differences.

Other significant findings

There were none.

Other data

Four collection centres provided data: Hungary, the Philippines, and Sweden (see Table 9), and Zaire (urban, 304 ± 12 mg/l;[a] rural, 417 ± 35 mg/l[a]). These values were generally somewhat higher than those reported by the reference laboratory.

---

[a] Mean $\pm$ SD for specimens collected 3 months after birth.

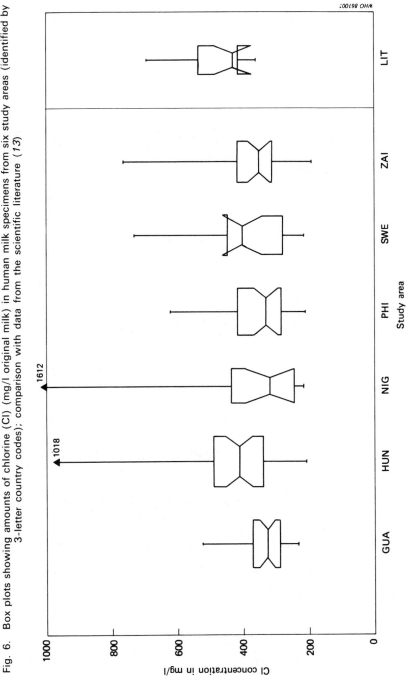

Fig. 6. Box plots showing amounts of chlorine (Cl) (mg/l original milk) in human milk specimens from six study areas (identified by 3-letter country codes); comparison with data from the scientific literature (13)

Table 9. Statistical summary of amounts of chlorine found in human milk (mg/l original milk)

Study area	Study group	No. of observations	Minimum	Percentiles 10	16	25	50 median	75	84	90	Maximum	SD (median) absolute	relative (%)
Data from reference analytical laboratory													
Guatemala	1	10	303	303	310	323	363	494	514	525	527	50	14
	2	9	248	248	249	263	290	395	425	433	433	41	14
	3	12	232	238	254	270	294	340	347	348	348	18	6
	All	31	232	250	270	288	326	371	415	478	527	14	4
Hungary	1	12	305	311	327	342	402	481	501	543	561	37	9
	2	11	206	225	295	339	436	476	500	508	510	38	9
	3	11	294	296	303	329	420	505	608	929	1018	49	12
	All	34	206	303	318	338	411	490	504	536	1018	24	6
Nigeria	1	5	224	224	224	228	297	479	507	507	507	104	35
	2	2	310	310	310	310	961	1612	1612	1612	1612	852	89
	3	9	215	215	222	254	326	387	423	470	470	41	13
	All	16	215	221	226	245	318	436	480	838	1612	44	14
Philippines	1	9	210	210	223	243	300	463	603	622	622	68	23
	2	11	221	224	235	285	363	417	429	520	545	37	10
	3	11	262	266	281	286	331	386	463	500	510	28	8
	All	31	210	232	255	283	329	416	454	538	622	22	7
Sweden	All	20	214	231	265	278	401	448	540	590	732	35	9
Zaire	1	12	232	243	270	298	350	378	452	523	551	21	6
	3	12	190	226	308	313	375	434	496	686	765	32	9
	All	24	190	250	293	311	350	417	459	526	765	20	6

Data from collection centres (for their own samples)

Hungary	1	21	380	382	411	435	460	515	540	598	670	16	4
	2	33	260	368	380	405	460	520	530	536	880	19	4
	3	27	270	348	365	380	450	570	595	622	900	34	8
	All	81	260	370	380	400	460	520	539	598	900	12	3
Philippines	1	19	234	251	276	351	431	602	675	745	886	53	12
	2	29	182	318	333	384	416	494	576	591	776	19	5
	3	27	167	199	291	318	401	468	500	521	563	27	7
	All	75	167	259	318	351	414	502	559	595	886	16	4
Sweden	All	28	281	465	501	513	580	679	707	752	823	29	5

Data from the literature

	All	11	360	363	374	414	430	536	589	670	693	34	8

Chromium

Graphite furnace atomic absorption spectrometry was used as the reference analytical method for chromium (see Annex 3). Despite the fact that this is a difficult element to measure reliably at the concentrations found in human and animal milk, and that no entirely appropriate certified reference materials for it were available, there are reasonable grounds for confidence in the accuracy of the analytical method used in this study. However, since, for most samples, concentrations were very close to the limit of detection by this method, the precision was very poor. The results obtained are presented in Table 10 and Fig. 7.

Differences between study areas

Most of the measured values were close to the detection limit of the method and the measurement errors were relatively large. Nevertheless, the available data show that, on the whole, specimens from the Philippines and Nigeria had relatively high chromium concentrations as compared with the other study areas.

Other significant findings

There were none.

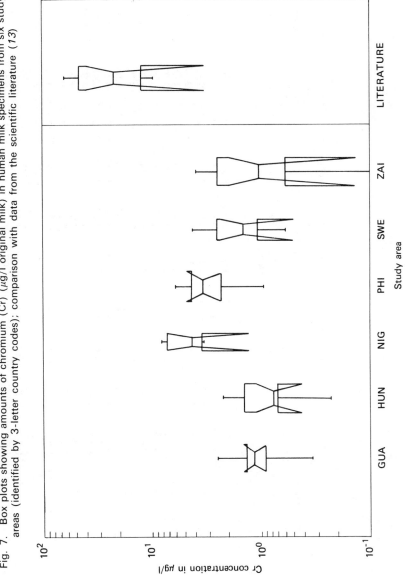

Fig. 7. Box plots showing amounts of chromium (Cr) (µg/l original milk) in human milk specimens from six study areas (identified by 3-letter country codes); comparison with data from the scientific literature (13)

Table 10. Statistical summary of amounts of chromium found in human milk (μg/l original milk)

Study area	Study group	No. of observations	Minimum[a]	Percentiles 10	16	25	50 median	75	84	90	Maximum	SD (median) absolute	relative (%)
Data from reference analytical laboratory													
Guatemala	1	2	1.22	1.22	1.22	1.22	1.32	1.43	1.43	1.43	1.43	0.14	10
	2	2	1.16	1.16	1.16	1.16	1.16	1.17	1.17	1.17	1.17	0.01	1
	3	5	0.34	0.34	0.34	0.51	1.17	1.91	2.52	2.52	2.52	0.58	50
	All	9	0.34	0.34	0.54	0.92	1.17	1.37	1.87	2.52	2.52	0.14	12
Hungary	1	4	0.71	0.71	0.71	0.71	0.81	1.31	1.45	1.45	1.45	0.28	34
	2	3	0.23	0.23	0.23	0.23	2.04	2.24	2.24	2.24	2.24	1.07	53
	3	4	0.66	0.66	0.66	0.68	0.77	0.80	0.81	0.81	0.81	0.05	7
	All	11	0.23	0.32	0.63	0.71	0.78	1.45	2.06	2.20	2.24	0.21	26
Nigeria	1	2	3.44	3.44	3.44	3.44	3.60	3.77	3.77	3.77	3.77	0.22	6
	2	1	4.94	4.94	4.94	4.94	4.94	4.94	4.94	4.94	4.94	0.00	0
	3	1	8.18	8.18	8.18	8.18	8.18	8.18	8.18	8.18	8.18	0.00	0
	All	4	3.44	3.44	3.44	3.52	4.35	7.37	8.18	8.18	8.18	1.78	41
Philippines	1	3	0.97	0.97	0.97	0.97	3.73	4.35	4.35	4.35	4.35	1.81	48
	2	3	2.45	2.45	2.45	2.45	3.93	4.55	4.55	4.55	4.55	1.12	29
	3	4	1.99	1.99	1.99	2.14	2.89	5.39	6.13	6.13	6.13	1.51	52
	All	10	0.97	1.07	1.75	2.33	3.46	4.40	4.93	5.97	6.13	0.60	17
Sweden	All	6	0.61	0.61	0.69	1.10	1.48	2.59	4.06	4.34	4.34	0.57	38
Zaire	1	5	0.61	0.61	0.61	0.72	0.88	1.07	1.08	1.08	1.08	0.14	16
	3	6	0.00	0.00	0.07	0.43	2.46	3.04	3.84	3.99	3.99	0.99	40
	All	11	0.00	0.12	0.53	0.61	1.07	2.57	2.83	3.74	3.99	0.55	51

Data from collection centres (for their own samples)

Hungary											
1	18	9.00	9.00	9.08	11.75	13.50	20.25	57.72	73.40	86.00	1.86	14
2	30	7.00	7.10	8.96	11.00	16.00	23.00	26.04	27.00	30.00	2.03	13
3	23	0.00	6.40	7.00	9.00	16.00	26.00	32.20	62.80	76.00	3.28	21
All	71	0.00	7.20	9.00	11.00	15.00	23.00	27.00	29.80	86.00	1.32	9

Data from the literature

All	8	10.00	10.00	10.88	12.75	22.90	47.75	61.00	66.50	66.50	11.46	50

[a] Zeros indicate values below the detection limit ~0.2–0.5 µg/l.

Cobalt

Instrumental neutron activation analysis was used as the reference analytical method for cobalt (see Annex 5). Despite the fact that this is a difficult element to measure reliably at the concentrations found in human and animal milk, and that no entirely appropriate certified reference materials for it were available, there are reasonable grounds for confidence in the analytical method used in this study. The results obtained are presented in Table 11 and Fig. 8.

Differences between study areas

Very significant differences between study areas were observed. Once again the Philippine values were considerably higher than those for any other study area. Nigerian values were also relatively high, while Hungarian values were relatively low.

Other significant findings

In Guatemala, the urban poor group had significantly higher values than the urban elite. In Zaire, the rural group had significantly higher values than the urban group. No other significant differences were observed.

Table 11.　Statistical summary of amounts of cobalt found in human milk (µg/l original milk)

Study area	Study group	No. of observations	Minimum	Percentiles							Maximum	SD (median)	
				10	16	25	50 median	75	84	90		absolute	relative (%)
Data from reference analytical laboratory													
Guatemala	1	21	0.07	0.09	0.10	0.13	0.17	0.28	0.55	0.80	1.63	0.03	18
	2	24	0.12	0.13	0.20	0.24	0.35	0.59	0.72	0.73	0.77	0.07	19
	3	39	0.05	0.14	0.17	0.19	0.24	0.62	1.81	2.87	2208	0.06	27
	All	84	0.05	0.13	0.14	0.17	0.24	0.52	0.72	1.28	2208	0.03	14
Hungary	1	21	0.02	0.04	0.07	0.10	0.17	0.25	0.55	0.70	3.68	0.03	18
	2	29	0.05	0.06	0.08	0.09	0.15	0.21	0.26	0.38	0.51	0.02	13
	3	21	0.07	0.07	0.08	0.09	0.12	0.21	0.25	0.26	0.28	0.02	20
	All	71	0.02	0.07	0.08	0.09	0.15	0.21	0.25	0.37	3.68	0.01	9
Nigeria	1	6	0.26	0.26	0.29	0.43	0.78	1.04	1.35	1.41	1.41	0.23	29
	2	2	0.59	0.59	0.59	0.59	0.72	0.85	0.85	0.85	0.85	0.17	24
	3	10	0.29	0.29	0.34	0.38	0.61	0.94	1.04	1.10	1.11	0.16	27
	All	18	0.26	0.28	0.35	0.40	0.64	0.91	1.01	1.14	1.41	0.11	18
Philippines	1	16	0.48	0.52	0.62	0.70	1.24	2.10	2.30	2.65	2.97	0.32	26
	2	28	0.67	0.74	0.86	0.94	1.43	2.66	3.07	3.36	4.74	0.30	21
	3	21	0.54	0.57	0.70	1.00	1.35	1.88	2.03	2.60	4.54	0.18	13
	All	65	0.48	0.67	0.75	0.94	1.40	1.97	2.61	2.98	4.74	0.12	8
Sweden	All	32	0.10	0.11	0.12	0.14	0.27	0.38	0.48	0.52	0.75	0.04	15
Zaire	1	37	0.09	0.13	0.14	0.15	0.28	0.41	0.56	0.66	1.80	0.04	14
	3	32	0.16	0.25	0.29	0.34	0.51	0.68	1.04	1.14	1.90	0.06	11
	All	69	0.09	0.15	0.16	0.21	0.36	0.58	0.68	1.05	1.90	0.04	12
Data from the literature													
	All	5	1.00	1.00	1.00	1.35	2.00	7.45	8.60	8.60	8.60	2.53	126

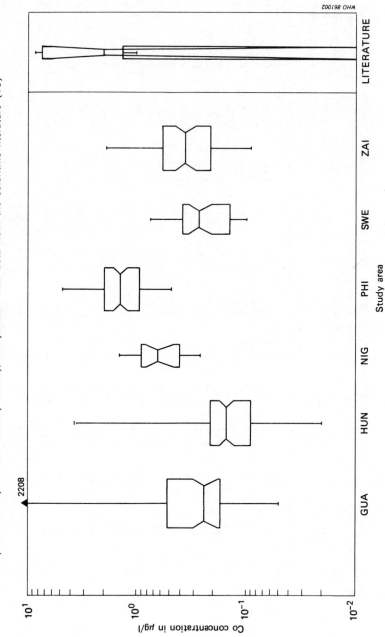

Fig. 8. Box plots showing amounts of cobalt (Co) (μg/l original milk) in human milk specimens from six study areas (identified by 3-letter country codes); comparison with data from the scientific literature (13)

Copper

Radiochemical neutron activation analysis was used as the reference analytical method for copper (see Annex 5). The quality assurance data obtained during the course of the project confirmed that this method had satisfactory accuracy and precision. The results obtained are presented in Table 12 and Fig. 9.

Differences between study areas

Several significant differences were observed, though in numerical terms they were not large. In general, Guatemala, Nigeria and the Philippines, had relatively high values, and the other study areas relatively low values.

Other significant findings

There were none.

Other data

Three collection centres provided data: Hungary, the Philippines and Sweden. The Philippine values were somewhat lower than those reported by the reference laboratory; for the other two collection centres the values were higher. It is assumed that the reasons for these discrepancies were analytical.

Table 12. Statistical summary of amounts of copper found in human milk (μg/l original milk)

Study area	Study group	No. of observations	Minimum	Percentiles							Maximum	SD (median)	
				10	16	25	50 median	75	84	90		absolute	relative (%)
Data from reference analytical laboratory													
Guatemala	1	21	116	164	176	196	246	285	314	323	348	18	7
	2	24	178	197	198	236	321	394	409	451	476	30	9
	3	39	140	178	193	215	261	317	333	362	431	15	6
	All	84	116	178	195	211	263	323	354	391	476	11	4
Hungary	1	21	77	134	148	167	199	256	294	303	358	18	9
	2	29	93	135	153	170	204	262	289	297	387	16	8
	3	21	93	112	132	152	195	249	284	301	306	19	8
	All	71	77	132	149	161	203	254	288	299	387	10	10
Nigeria	1	6	208	208	209	214	258	355	377	381	381	54	21
	2	2	257	257	257	257	273	290	290	290	290	22	8
	3	10	103	115	193	232	279	348	379	432	440	34	12
	All	18	103	197	216	232	278	345	360	387	440	25	9
Philippines	1	16	140	167	221	251	281	344	375	423	457	21	8
	2	28	172	217	237	251	349	444	455	464	485	34	10
	3	17	174	176	187	204	339	383	395	405	430	40	12
	All	61	140	190	218	249	310	397	435	451	485	18	6
Sweden	All	31	80	88	102	108	186	279	302	320	408	29	15
Zaire	1	37	57	98	103	128	202	287	316	357	638	24	12
	3	31	119	132	141	157	199	306	336	415	715	25	12
	All	68	57	107	126	150	201	288	329	360	715	16	8

Data from collection centres (for their own samples)

Hungary	1	18	118	148	153	167	234	352	376	421	744	40	17
	2	31	148	185	216	242	310	474	648	809	1020	39	12
	3	21	160	168	180	191	231	420	469	505	680	46	20
	All	70	118	166	181	213	263	400	477	648	1020	21	8
Philippines	1	19	135	180	180	180	270	315	319	355	405	29	11
	2	29	90	90	134	175	225	287	323	405	495	19	9
	3	27	90	90	132	135	180	225	270	320	355	16	9
	All	75	90	130	135	170	225	275	315	334	495	11	5
Sweden	All	28	160	190	200	220	250	307	314	333	370	15	6

Data from the literature

	All	34	40	183	219	236	280	402	424	445	640	26	9

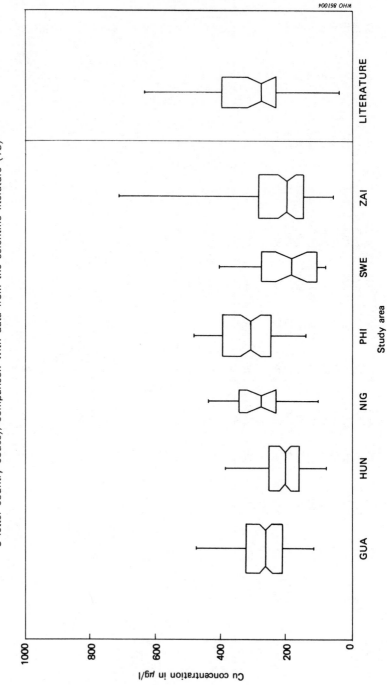

Fig. 9.   Box plots showing amounts of copper (Cu) (µg/l original milk) in human milk specimens from six study areas (identified by 3-letter country codes); comparison with data from the scientific literature (13)

Fluorine

An electrochemical method, using a fluoride-selective electrode, was used as the reference analytical method for fluorine (see Annex 8). Despite the fact that this is a difficult element to measure reliably at the concentrations found in human milk, and that no entirely appropriate certified reference materials for it were available, there are reasonable grounds for confidence in the analytical method used in this study. The results obtained are presented in Table 13 and Fig. 10.

Differences between study areas

The Philippine values were considerably higher than those from any other study area. In contrast, values for Guatemala and, particularly, for Zaire were relatively low.

Other significant findings

In the Philippines, specimens collected during the fourth trimester had significantly lower fluorine concentrations than those collected during the second and third trimesters.

Table 13. Statistical summary of amounts of fluorine found in human milk (μg/l original milk)

Study area	Study group	No. of observations	Minimum	Percentiles							Maximum	SD (median)	
				10	16	25	50 median	75	84	90		absolute	relative (%)
Data from reference analytical laboratory													
Guatemala	1	8	6.0	6.0	6.6	7.6	11.5	29.8	56.4	73.8	73.8	7.3	63
	2	7	7.1	7.1	7.3	7.8	9.7	11.1	13.6	14.6	14.6	1.1	12
	3	14	6.1	6.3	6.8	7.5	9.3	10.0	10.4	16.8	23.1	0.6	7
	All	29	6.0	6.6	7.1	7.7	9.4	10.9	14.9	23.1	73.8	0.5	6
Hungary	1	18	7.7	8.6	9.1	10.3	13.6	17.4	20.3	22.4	31.6	1.5	11
	2	28	5.7	8.6	9.3	9.7	13.6	16.2	19.2	21.3	31.3	1.1	8
	3	17	9.7	10.3	10.6	11.5	13.9	18.2	22.3	30.2	33.7	1.5	11
	All	63	5.7	9.1	9.7	10.5	13.8	17.1	19.7	21.4	33.7	0.8	6
Nigeria	1	2	13.2	13.2	13.2	13.2	19.9	26.5	26.5	26.5	26.5	8.7	44
	2	1	46.6	46.6	46.6	46.6	46.6	46.6	46.6	46.6	46.6	0.0	0
	3	7	8.8	8.8	9.0	9.7	23.0	44.9	57.4	62.3	62.3	12.3	54
	All	10	8.8	8.9	9.5	12.4	24.7	45.3	50.4	60.7	62.3	9.7	39
Philippines	1	6	74.8	74.8	75.0	75.9	142.9	162.5	172.1	173.9	173.9	32.7	23
	2	17	18.9	42.1	75.8	81.9	116.6	162.7	174.2	193.8	214.2	18.1	16
	3	9	28.9	28.9	32.0	36.9	101.6	122.4	131.9	145.1	145.1	26.4	26
	All	32	18.9	35.7	51.6	77.1	117.7	155.0	163.2	173.4	214.2	12.8	11
Sweden	All	10	10.1	10.3	11.3	13.7	17.0	20.1	21.4	21.4	21.4	1.9	11
Zaire	1	35	0.0	0.0	0.0	0.0	5.7	9.3	10.8	13.7	17.9	1.5	25
	3	26	0.0	3.9	5.8	6.1	7.5	10.2	11.7	13.1	27.5	0.7	10
	All	61	0.0	0.0	0.0	4.9	6.8	9.7	11.3	12.6	27.5	0.6	8
Data from the literature													
	All	8	4.0	4.0	4.4	5.5	16.5	51.7	66.4	77.0	77.0	15.1	92

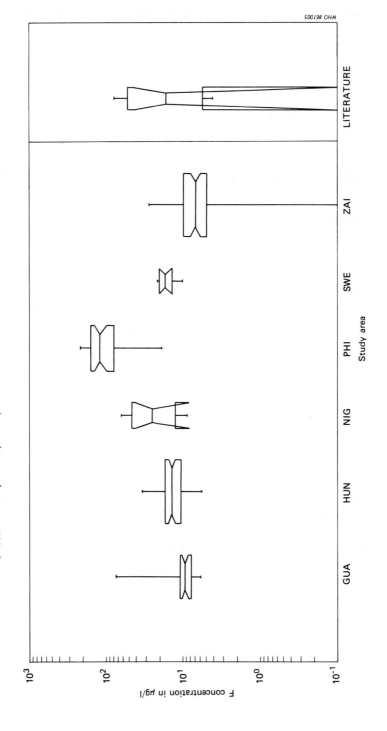

Fig. 10. Box plots showing amounts of fluorine (F) (μg/l original milk) in human milk specimens from six study areas (identified by 3-letter country codes); comparison with data from the scientific literature (13)

Iodine

Radiochemical neutron activation analysis was used as the reference analytical method for iodine (see Annex 7). Despite the fact that this is a difficult element to measure reliably at the concentrations found in human and animal milk, and that no entirely appropriate certified reference materials for it were available, there are reasonable grounds for confidence in the analytical method used in this study. The results obtained are presented in Table 14 and Fig. 11.

Differences between study areas

The data from Zaire showed a relatively low median value and large variability.

Other significant findings

In Guatemala, values for the urban poor group were significantly lower than for the urban elite group. In Sweden, specimens collected during the fourth trimester had significantly higher iodine concentrations than specimens collected during the first trimester.

Table 14. Statistical summary of amounts of iodine found in human milk (μg/l original milk)

Study area	Study group	No. of observations	Minimum	Percentiles 10	16	25	50 median	75	84	90	Maximum	SD (median) absolute	relative (%)
Data from reference analytical laboratory													
Guatemala	1	8	47	47	48	52	90	115	1363	2342	2342	21	23
	2	8	23	23	24	26	35	55	63	66	66	9	27
	3	9	3	3	9	24	63	125	163	184	184	31	49
	All	25	3	19	26	33	60	103	116	163	2342	13	22
Hungary	1	10	21	22	24	31	59	87	93	95	96	17	28
	2	14	17	22	28	40	74	103	146	179	192	16	21
	3	7	11	11	11	13	64	88	118	129	129	26	41
	All	31	11	18	25	32	64	88	99	126	192	9	14
Nigeria	1	2	62	62	62	62	74	86	86	86	86	16	21
	2	1	53	53	53	53	53	53	53	53	53	0	0
	3	4	13	13	13	16	44	109	124	124	124	43	97
	All	7	13	13	16	25	62	86	113	124	124	21	34
Philippines	1	5	33	33	33	36	57	107	131	131	131	29	51
	2	3	15	15	15	15	35	86	86	86	86	38	108
	3	3	26	26	26	26	62	73	73	73	73	25	41
	All	11	15	17	25	33	57	83	89	122	131	14	24
Sweden	All	16	17	18	27	33	56	81	137	151	172	11	20
Zaire	1	10	3	3	4	5	9	17	153	515	570	3	37
	3	9	7	7	8	12	25	112	686	1537	1537	31	124
	All	19	3	5	6	7	15	32	116	570	1537	5	36
Data from the literature													
	All	3	60	60	60	60	70	70	70	70	70	5	8

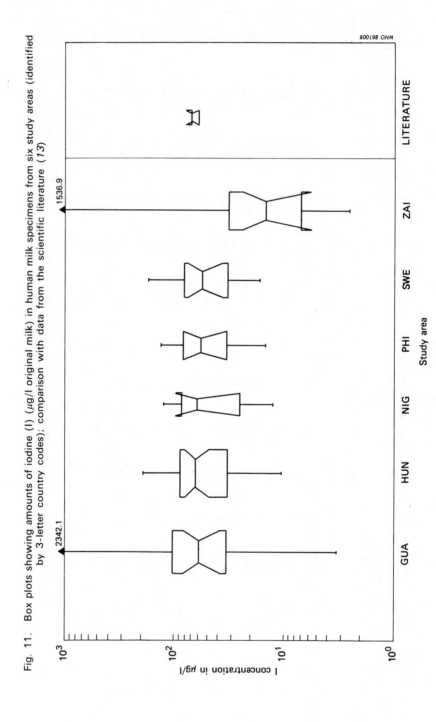

Fig. 11. Box plots showing amounts of iodine (I) (μg/l original milk) in human milk specimens from six study areas (identified by 3-letter country codes); comparison with data from the scientific literature (13)

Iron

Instrumental neutron activation analysis was used as the reference analytical method for iron (see Annex 5). The quality assurance data obtained during the course of the project confirmed that, as far as could be judged, this method was working reliably, though further independent confirmation of its accuracy would be desirable. The results obtained are presented in Table 15 and Fig. 12.

Differences between study areas

Several significant differences were observed, though in numerical terms they were not large. Once again the Philippine values were relatively high. The values for Guatemala and Hungary, on the other hand, were relatively low.

Other significant findings

In Guatemala, the rural group had significantly lower values than either of the urban groups, while in Zaire, the rural group had significantly higher values than the urban group. In Hungary, the two urban groups differed significantly from each other (mothers with university education > mothers with only primary education).

Other data

Three collection centres reported data: Hungary, the Philippines, and Sweden. In all cases the agreement with the reference laboratory was poor, presumably for analytical reasons.

Table 15. Statistical summary of amounts of iron found in human milk (μg/l original milk)

Study area	Study group	No. of observations	Minimum	Percentiles 10	16	25	50 median	75	84	90	Maximum	SD (median) absolute	relative (%)
Data from reference analytical laboratory													
Guatemala	1	21	202	227	232	287	385	443	512	682	860	32	8
	2	24	180	196	213	283	435	627	678	720	865	65	15
	3	39	101	108	138	171	239	379	461	474	1010	31	13
	All	84	101	161	186	214	346	462	511	636	1010	25	7
Hungary	1	21	265	281	291	326	494	559	592	690	1908	47	10
	2	29	173	207	223	259	343	427	505	587	633	29	8
	3	21	180	235	265	288	377	491	542	590	654	41	11
	All	71	173	230	265	289	365	501	559	589	1908	23	6
Nigeria	1	6	296	296	307	367	539	1064	1654	1767	1767	264	49
	2	2	602	602	602	602	826	1050	1050	1050	1050	294	36
	3	10	273	278	310	349	487	614	628	642	644	78	16
	All	18	273	294	323	382	523	637	823	1122	1767	56	11
Philippines	1	16	327	333	445	520	775	1252	1367	1456	1525	170	22
	2	28	128	269	347	505	741	1057	1169	1244	1870	97	13
	3	21	306	339	401	470	642	836	1009	1080	1230	74	11
	All	65	128	333	403	504	720	1058	1154	1252	1870	64	9
Sweden	All	32	205	275	303	343	446	556	655	759	1049	35	8
Zaire	1	37	142	211	234	304	388	538	688	1037	1501	36	9
	3	32	384	494	542	592	851	1349	1423	1498	1997	124	15
	All	69	142	258	312	375	556	1035	1286	1408	1997	74	13

Data from collection centres, (for their own samples)

Hungary	1	19	312	669	894	1090	1260	2150	3360	4170	5190	225	18
	2	31	332	494	597	800	1380	1950	3198	4802	5170	191	14
	3	22	480	865	999	1067	1390	1967	2414	3881	4630	178	13
	All	72	312	602	801	983	1370	1942	2476	4122	5190	105	8
Philippines	1	17	30	30	30	80	100	350	420	440	520	61	61
	2	29	60	100	100	100	180	350	364	420	540	43	24
	3	27	30	30	60	100	180	350	420	480	520	45	25
	All	73	30	60	80	100	180	350	420	420	540	27	15
Sweden	All	28	140	150	190	210	260	327	371	414	610	21	8

Data from the literature

	All	33	150	195	244	359	450	800	1123	1338	1500	71	16

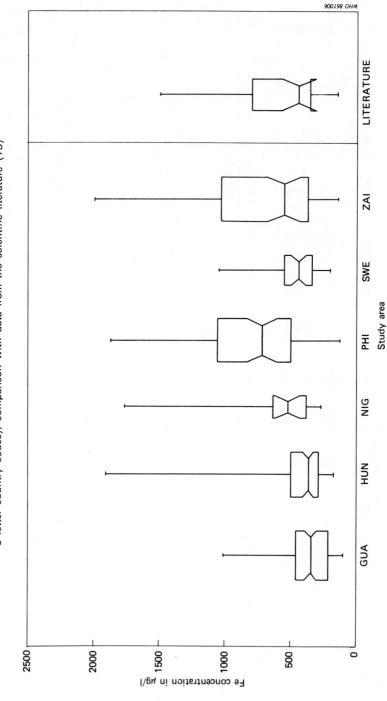

Fig. 12. Box plots showing amounts of iron (Fe) (μg/l original milk) in human milk specimens from six study areas (identified by 3-letter country codes); comparison with data from the scientific literature (13)

Lead

Electrothermal atomization atomic absorption spectrometry was used as the reference analytical method for lead (see Annex 6). Although there are no *a priori* reasons for doubting the reliability of the analytical data, some quality assurance problems were encountered, and further independent confirmation of the accuracy of the analyses would be desirable. The results obtained are presented in Table 16 and Fig. 13.

Differences between study areas

The data appear to fall into two groups. Hungary, the Philippines and Sweden all had relatively high values and narrow total ranges; the other study areas all had relatively low values and wide total ranges.

Other significant findings

There were none.

Other data

Two collection centres provided data: Hungary and Sweden. The Hungarian data were comparable to those reported by the reference laboratory, while the Swedish values were much lower. It is assumed that this discrepancy is due to analytical problems, since lead is apparently a difficult element to determine reliably in milk (*14*).

Table 16. Statistical summary of amounts of lead found in human milk ($\mu g/l$ original milk)

Study area	Study group	No. of observations	Minimum[a]	Percentiles							Maximum	SD (median)	
				10	16	25	50 median	75	84	90		absolute	relative (%)
Data from reference analytical laboratory													
Guatemala	1	12	0.0	0.0	0.0	0.4	2.9	3.8	4.3	5.4	5.9	0.9	31
	2	24	0.0	0.0	0.0	0.0	3.3	6.9	8.3	9.6	12.2	1.3	40
	3	38	0.0	0.0	0.0	0.9	2.8	5.7	6.6	9.0	15.4	0.7	26
	All	74	0.0	0.0	0.0	0.0	2.9	5.2	6.7	8.4	15.4	0.6	19
Hungary	1	20	7.1	11.0	11.4	12.1	17.8	23.9	27.1	30.8	33.2	2.4	14
	2	28	5.5	8.6	9.2	11.2	14.6	18.6	20.5	27.9	33.6	1.3	9
	3	20	7.1	9.0	9.9	10.2	14.3	22.9	29.2	35.3	113.4	2.6	18
	All	68	5.5	9.1	10.1	11.4	14.9	19.6	25.0	29.9	113.4	0.9	6
Nigeria	1	5	3.8	3.8	3.8	4.3	8.4	14.7	20.3	20.3	20.3	4.3	51
	2	1	9.5	9.5	9.5	9.5	9.5	9.5	9.5	9.5	9.5	0.0	0
	3	8	0.0	0.0	0.7	2.1	4.1	7.2	8.0	8.1	8.1	1.7	41
	All	14	0.0	0.8	2.4	3.7	4.9	8.6	9.3	14.9	20.3	1.2	25
Philippines	1	14	10.7	10.9	11.2	11.5	16.6	20.4	22.7	57.3	91.8	2.2	13
	2	28	4.7	5.0	8.3	9.1	16.0	19.3	21.1	22.3	71.9	1.8	11
	3	21	7.8	8.8	10.9	13.8	17.0	40.7	81.6	108.1	140.6	5.4	32
	All	63	4.7	8.4	9.3	11.3	16.6	21.8	24.0	55.2	140.6	1.2	7
Sweden	All	32	9.6	12.5	13.4	14.4	16.8	20.5	23.5	26.9	37.0	1.0	6
Zaire	1	37	0.0	0.0	0.0	1.1	3.1	8.5	11.1	18.1	41.1	1.1	36
	3	32	0.0	0.0	2.0	2.9	6.0	9.5	11.2	14.3	19.5	1.1	18
	All	69	0.0	0.0	0.0	1.9	5.0	8.9	11.1	15.7	41.1	0.8	16

	n											
Data from collection centres (for their own samples)												
Hungary												
1	18	0.0	0.0	0.0	0.0	20.0	59.7	132.8	195.6	219.0	13.0	65
2	31	0.0	0.0	0.0	6.0	25.0	44.0	72.3	82.8	190.0	6.3	25
3	23	0.0	0.0	0.0	0.0	16.0	62.0	99.2	157.8	189.0	12.0	75
All	72	0.0	0.0	0.0	0.0	22.5	44.7	77.5	132.2	219.0	4.9	22
Sweden												
All	38	0.5	1.0	1.0	1.7	2.0	3.0	4.0	4.1	6.0	0.2	9
Data from the literature												
All	9	2.0	2.0	8.0	16.0	22.5	34.0	190.8	420.0	420.0	5.6	25

[a] Zeros indicate values below the detection limit (~ 1 µg/l)

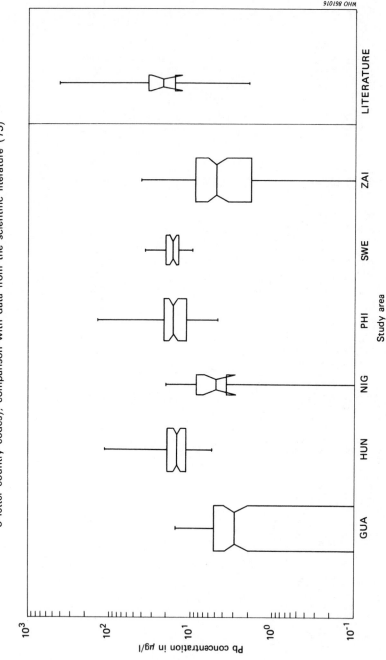

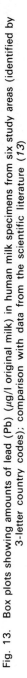

Fig. 13. Box plots showing amounts of lead (Pb) (µg/l original milk) in human milk specimens from six study areas (identified by 3-letter country codes); comparison with data from the scientific literature (13)

Magnesium

Flame atomic absorption spectrometry was used as the reference analytical method for magnesium (see Annex 3). The quality assurance data obtained during the course of the study confirmed that this method was working with satisfactory accuracy and precision. The results obtained are presented in Table 17 and Fig. 14.

Differences between study areas

Several significant differences were observed, the Zairian values being relatively high, and the Nigerian and Philippine values relatively low. In numerical terms, however, the magnitude of these differences was not large.

Other significant findings

No significant differences were apparent, though there is some evidence that, in Guatemala, the rural group may have had somewhat higher values than the urban groups.

Other data

Three collection centres provided data: Hungary, the Philippines and Sweden. In all cases, the agreement with the reference laboratory was fairly satisfactory.

Table 17. Statistical summary of amounts of magnesium found in human milk (mg/l original milk)

Study area	Study group	No. of observations	Minimum	Percentiles							Maximum	SD (median)	
				10	16	25	50 median	75	84	90		absolute	relative (%)
Data from reference analytical laboratory													
Guatemala	1	22	22.7	24.3	25.2	26.7	31.8	36.0	39.0	39.2	46.8	1.8	6
	2	22	9.5	22.8	24.9	27.4	32.7	35.9	38.7	41.0	51.2	1.7	5
	3	37	26.3	30.6	31.0	32.6	37.5	40.8	42.9	44.1	55.7	1.2	3
	All	81	9.5	25.8	27.5	30.0	34.1	39.0	40.5	42.9	55.7	0.9	3
Hungary	1	21	24.5	25.5	26.9	29.9	33.4	37.1	39.8	45.4	46.5	1.5	4
	2	29	23.3	24.2	25.1	29.2	32.6	36.4	39.1	39.4	42.5	1.2	4
	3	21	24.0	24.8	25.9	27.5	32.3	34.9	36.9	38.9	41.3	1.5	5
	All	71	23.3	24.9	26.0	29.1	32.6	35.8	38.2	39.4	46.5	0.7	2
Nigeria	1	5	16.0	16.0	16.0	18.1	25.2	31.8	34.7	34.7	34.7	5.7	23
	2	1	26.5	26.5	26.5	26.5	26.5	26.5	26.5	26.5	26.5	0.0	0
	3	9	15.0	15.0	19.9	25.9	32.2	34.1	36.2	39.3	39.3	2.5	8
	All	15	15.0	15.6	18.4	23.2	29.0	34.0	34.4	36.5	39.3	2.6	9
Philippines	1	16	19.6	21.6	22.5	25.0	27.9	36.0	37.0	38.1	39.9	2.6	9
	2	28	19.2	23.5	24.9	26.0	30.6	31.4	32.3	34.4	35.8	1.0	3
	3	21	18.6	21.5	23.4	25.4	28.0	32.2	33.2	34.2	38.5	1.4	5
	All	65	18.6	22.7	24.4	25.4	29.7	31.9	33.7	35.7	39.9	0.7	3
Sweden	All	29	19.6	28.4	28.9	30.1	34.2	43.8	45.8	49.7	59.7	2.3	7
Zaire	1	37	19.6	22.6	29.2	32.7	36.7	39.3	40.6	42.7	46.4	1.0	3
	3	32	24.3	31.8	33.7	34.8	38.9	43.9	48.7	54.3	62.5	1.5	4
	All	69	19.6	26.8	32.6	33.7	37.8	41.4	43.9	46.4	62.5	0.9	2

Data from collection centres (for their own samples)

Hungary	1	18	14.0	14.9	18.0	19.7	27.0	30.0	31.0	32.3	35.0	2.2	8
	2	31	11.0	16.0	16.0	18.0	27.0	31.0	33.0	35.6	50.0	2.2	8
	3	22	12.0	16.3	17.7	21.2	28.5	34.2	35.0	35.7	36.0	2.6	9
	All	71	11.0	16.0	17.0	19.0	28.0	31.0	34.0	35.0	50.0	1.3	5
Philippines	1	19	18.0	18.0	19.0	22.0	23.0	27.0	28.9	30.2	31.8	1.1	5
	2	29	16.0	19.0	19.0	22.5	24.2	26.0	27.1	29.0	33.0	0.6	2
	3	27	14.0	18.0	18.5	20.0	23.0	25.5	26.5	28.3	30.5	1.0	4
	All	75	14.0	18.5	19.0	21.5	23.5	26.0	27.0	29.0	33.0	0.5	2
Sweden	All	28	25.0	28.8	29.7	31.4	37.4	41.9	43.8	44.7	48.2	1.8	5

Data from the literature

	All	22	14.0	24.2	26.0	26.0	30.2	33.5	37.1	39.2	40.2	1.5	5

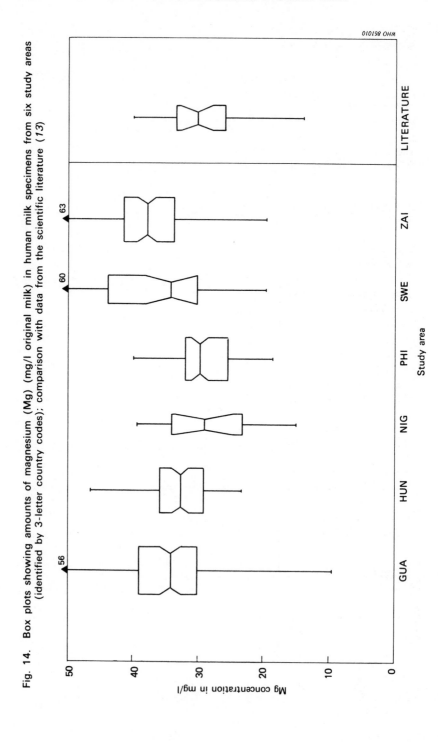

Fig. 14. Box plots showing amounts of magnesium (Mg) (mg/l original milk) in human milk specimens from six study areas (identified by 3-letter country codes); comparison with data from the scientific literature (13)

Manganese

Radiochemical neutron activation analysis was used as the reference analytical method for manganese (see Annex 5). The quality assurance data obtained during the course of the project confirmed that this method had satisfactory accuracy and precision. The results obtained are presented in Table 18 and Fig. 15.

Differences between study areas

Several significant differences were observed. Once again, the Philippine values were by far the highest. In contrast, Guatemala, Hungary, and Sweden all had relatively low values. Altogether, the data covered a very wide range (1–153 $\mu g/1$).

Other significant findings

In Guatemala, the urban poor group had significantly higher values than the other groups. In Zaire, the rural group had very much higher values than the urban group. In the Philippines, the rural group had significantly lower values than the urban elite group, and specimens collected during the fourth trimester had lower manganese concentrations than specimens collected during the third trimester.

Table 18. Statistical summary of amounts of manganese found in human milk (µg/l original milk)

Study area	Study group	No. of observations	Minimum	Percentiles							Maximum	SD (median)	
				10	16	25	50 median	75	84	90		absolute	relative (%)
Data from reference analytical laboratory													
Guatemala	1	21	2.05	2.13	2.18	2.51	3.23	4.67	5.37	5.76	19.98	0.44	13
	2	24	2.11	2.77	3.32	3.65	5.25	6.85	8.83	10.11	11.14	0.60	12
	3	39	1.40	2.24	2.41	2.60	3.50	5.38	6.63	25.93	70.29	0.41	12
	All	84	1.40	2.22	2.46	2.79	3.79	5.62	6.78	9.01	70.29	0.29	8
Hungary	1	21	1.68	1.93	2.25	2.62	4.94	9.60	12.60	15.48	17.91	1.41	29
	2	29	1.66	2.07	2.14	2.36	3.56	5.98	6.96	9.87	17.10	0.62	17
	3	21	1.06	1.96	2.29	2.83	3.64	7.38	8.15	12.99	16.51	0.92	25
	All	71	1.06	2.08	2.16	2.48	4.00	6.58	8.15	12.95	17.91	0.45	11
Nigeria	1	6	10.20	10.20	10.38	11.31	16.70	33.41	35.85	36.32	36.32	8.35	50
	2	2	22.88	22.88	22.88	22.88	25.97	29.07	29.07	29.07	29.07	4.05	16
	3	10	4.13	4.43	6.40	8.89	12.24	28.00	32.23	41.80	43.25	5.60	46
	All	18	4.13	6.82	9.49	10.03	15.84	28.83	32.30	37.01	43.25	4.10	26
Philippines	1	16	6.12	14.99	25.17	32.57	51.26	61.02	67.29	71.56	78.00	6.59	13
	2	28	5.90	12.97	20.92	25.97	41.11	62.27	73.72	81.91	153.4	6.35	15
	3	19	8.42	13.05	15.29	19.36	29.75	37.07	49.29	55.38	65.76	3.76	13
	All	63	5.90	13.64	19.64	24.80	39.55	55.15	65.49	71.68	153.4	3.54	9
Sweden	All	31	1.51	1.93	2.40	2.47	3.23	4.07	4.72	10.61	26.12	0.27	8
Zaire	1	37	1.91	2.49	2.83	3.30	4.55	9.75	12.52	18.30	27.31	0.98	22
	3	31	7.52	10.30	11.84	13.52	26.16	43.06	51.51	56.62	115.3	4.91	19
	All	68	1.91	2.95	3.35	4.36	11.21	26.17	30.59	46.42	115.3	2.45	22
Data from collection centres (for their own samples)													
Hungary	1	18	10.00	11.80	12.00	12.75	18.00	25.25	33.68	34.30	37.00	2.73	15
	2	31	8.00	12.00	12.00	13.00	19.00	29.00	43.20	72.20	88.00	2.66	14
	3	21	7.00	9.20	11.04	13.00	16.00	27.00	34.88	42.80	102	2.83	18
	All	70	7.00	12.00	12.00	13.00	18.00	27.25	33.28	43.40	102	1.58	9
Data from the literature													
	All	15	14.00	14.60	15.00	18.00	20.00	24.00	31.60	72.00	120	1.43	7

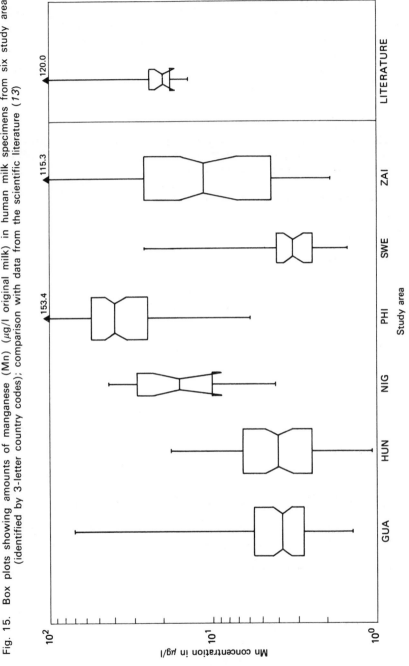

Fig. 15. Box plots showing amounts of manganese (Mn) (μg/l original milk) in human milk specimens from six study areas (identified by 3-letter country codes); comparison with data from the scientific literature (13)

WHO 861011

Mercury

Instrumental neutron activation analysis was used as the reference method for mercury (see Annex 5). Although there are no *a priori* reasons for doubting the reliability of the analytical data, some quality assurance problems were encountered, and further independent confirmation of the accuracy of the analyses would be desirable. The results obtained are presented in Table 19 and Fig. 16.

Differences between study areas

The median values all fell within a fairly narrow range, differing only by a factor of just over two between the lowest and the highest. Nevertheless, the Swedish values stand out in two respects; they were significantly higher than those for most other study areas; and they covered the smallest total range of values.

Other significant findings

There were none.

Table 19. Statistical summary of amounts of mercury found in human milk (μg/l original milk)

Study area	Study group	No. of observations	Minimum[a]	Percentiles 10	16	25	50 median	75	84	90	Maximum	SD (median) absolute	relative (%)
Data from reference analytical laboratory													
Guatemala	1	21	0.96	1.07	1.09	1.28	2.61	3.53	3.76	4.10	13.81	0.45	17
	2	24	0.27	0.46	0.62	0.80	1.39	2.14	2.53	3.38	3.77	0.25	18
	3	39	0.00	0.57	0.64	0.88	1.54	2.24	2.64	2.90	4.07	0.20	13
	All	84	0.00	0.62	0.78	0.93	1.56	2.55	3.08	3.53	13.81	0.16	11
Hungary	1	21	0.00	0.58	0.91	0.95	1.67	1.90	2.23	2.51	3.03	0.19	11
	2	29	0.26	0.54	0.76	0.89	1.51	2.76	3.29	3.79	10.94	0.32	21
	3	21	0.10	0.45	0.62	0.84	1.29	2.41	3.13	3.93	4.66	0.32	25
	All	71	0.00	0.55	0.78	0.92	1.43	2.37	2.86	3.35	10.94	0.16	11
Nigeria	1	6	1.45	1.45	1.65	2.70	3.92	5.82	7.77	8.14	8.14	1.18	30
	2	2	3.01	3.01	3.01	3.01	25.53	48.05	48.05	48.05	48.05	29.49	116
	3	10	0.87	0.90	1.05	1.16	1.51	2.13	2.53	3.45	3.59	0.28	19
	All	18	0.87	1.09	1.17	1.28	2.15	3.84	5.02	12.13	48.05	0.56	26
Philippines	1	16	0.51	0.93	1.12	1.22	2.36	3.71	4.71	7.89	11.98	0.58	24
	2	25	0.75	0.91	1.19	1.44	2.52	4.14	5.29	6.82	11.34	0.50	20
	3	24	0.00	0.37	0.68	0.98	1.45	2.95	4.19	4.96	6.92	0.37	26
	All	65	0.00	0.79	1.00	1.17	1.71	3.77	4.47	5.68	11.98	0.30	17
Sweden	All	32	1.03	1.69	1.85	2.19	3.34	4.22	5.02	5.53	7.74	0.33	10
Zaire	1	37	1.13	1.44	1.53	1.75	2.65	5.11	7.89	25.45	257.1	0.51	19
	3	32	0.64	0.98	1.38	1.68	3.05	15.37	24.56	48.56	118.4	2.24	73
	All	69	0.64	1.34	1.49	1.73	2.66	7.62	19.39	31.92	257.1	0.66	25
Data from the literature													
	All	5	0.93	0.93	0.93	2.06	3.30	7.37	7.60	7.60	7.60	2.20	67

[a] Zeros indicate values below the detection limit (~ 0.5 μg/l).

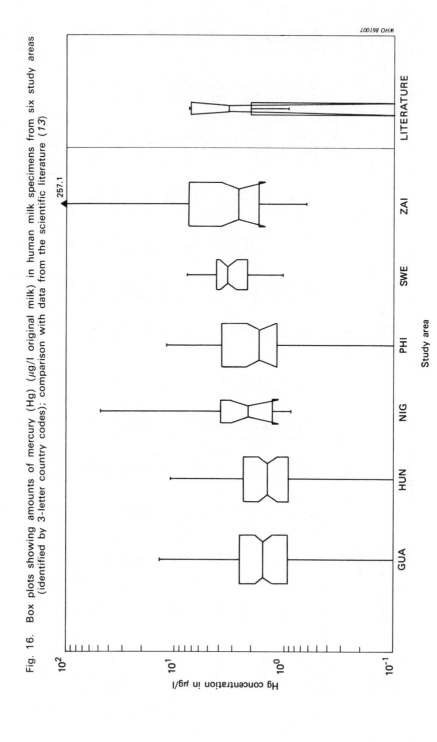

Fig. 16. Box plots showing amounts of mercury (Hg) (μg/l original milk) in human milk specimens from six study areas (identified by 3-letter country codes); comparison with data from the scientific literature (13)

Molybdenum

Radiochemical neutron activation analysis was used as the reference analytical method for molybdenum (see Annex 4). Measurements of various quality control materials confirmed that, as far as could be judged, this method was accurate. However, some of the milk samples contained molybdenum at levels close to, or below, the limit of detection. For this reason it was not always possible to obtain meaningful values for the medians and other statistical parameters. The results obtained are presented in Table 20 and Fig. 17.

Differences between study areas

Although some of the milk specimens contained molybdenum at concentrations below the detection limit of the method, it is nevertheless clear that specimens from the Philippines were characterized by having much higher concentrations than those from other study areas.

Other significant findings

In Zaire, specimens collected during the third trimester contained significantly lower molybdenum concentrations than those collected during the second trimester.

Table 20. Statistical summary of amounts of molybdenum found in human milk (μg/l original milk)

Study area	Study group	No. of obser-vations	Minimum[a]	Percentiles							Maximum	SD (median)	
				10	16	25	50 median	75	84	90		absolute	relative (%)
Data from reference analytical laboratory													
Guatemala	1	4	0.00	0.00	0.00	0.30	2.18	7.54	9.00	9.00	9.00	3.35	154
	2	3	0.00	0.00	0.00	0.00	4.45	5.53	5.53	5.53	5.53	2.96	67
	3	7	0.61	0.61	0.66	0.77	1.57	3.17	3.76	3.99	3.99	0.84	54
	All	14	0.00	0.00	0.00	0.73	2.12	4.11	5.10	7.27	9.00	0.84	39
Hungary	1	4	0.00	0.00	0.00	0.00	0.30	2.21	2.75	2.75	2.75	1.03	341
	2	5	0.00	0.00	0.00	0.00	0.00	2.24	3.70	3.70	3.70	0.93	
	3	4	0.00	0.00	0.00	0.00	0.00	2.91	3.88	3.88	3.88	1.35	
	All	13	0.00	0.00	0.00	0.00	0.00	1.77	3.48	3.81	3.88	0.45	
Nigeria	1	4	0.34	0.34	0.34	0.86	2.53	2.92	3.01	3.01	3.01	0.96	38
	2	2	2.17	2.17	2.17	2.17	3.68	5.20	5.20	5.20	5.20	1.99	54
	3	3	1.62	1.62	1.62	1.62	2.88	9.71	9.71	9.71	9.71	4.32	150
	All	9	0.34	0.34	1.11	1.90	2.65	4.10	7.00	9.71	9.71	0.68	26
Philippines	1	5	11.21	11.21	11.21	13.64	25.53	31.42	35.41	35.41	35.41	7.36	29
	2	6	6.75	6.75	7.68	12.57	18.11	22.70	26.96	27.78	27.78	3.83	21
	3	4	8.12	8.12	8.12	8.33	10.37	24.10	28.20	28.20	28.20	7.31	70
	All	15	6.75	7.57	8.57	11.21	16.36	27.43	27.96	31.08	35.41	3.88	24
Sweden	All	10	0.00	0.00	0.00	0.00	0.40	1.08	2.32	5.41	5.87	0.32	80
Zaire	1	7	0.00	0.00	0.00	0.00	0.00	2.40	3.03	3.28	3.28	0.84	
	3	8	0.00	0.00	0.00	0.35	1.97	4.03	5.05	5.81	5.81	1.21	61
	All	15	0.00	0.00	0.00	0.00	1.39	3.28	3.94	4.78	5.81	0.78	57
Data from the literature													
	All	1					15.00						

[a] Zeros indicate values below the detection limit (~ 0.3 μg/l).

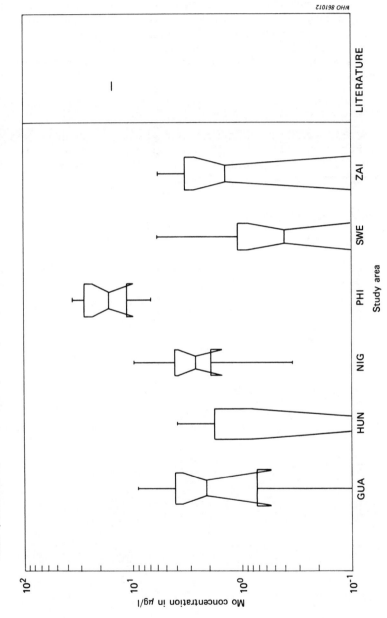

Fig. 17. Box plots showing amounts of molybdenum (Mo) (µg/l original milk) in human milk specimens from six study areas (identified by 3-letter country codes); comparison with data from the scientific literature (13)

Nickel

Inductively coupled plasma optical emission spectrometry was used as the reference analytical method for nickel (see Annex 6). Although there are no *a priori* reasons for doubting the reliability of the analytical data, some quality assurance problems were encountered, and further independent confirmation of the accuracy of the analyses would be desirable. The results obtained are presented in Table 21 and Fig. 18.

Differences between study areas

Several significant differences were observed, though the range of median values (4.9–16.1 µg/l) was numerically not very large. The values from Zaire appeared, on the whole, to be relatively low, though covering a wide total range.

Other significant findings

There were none.

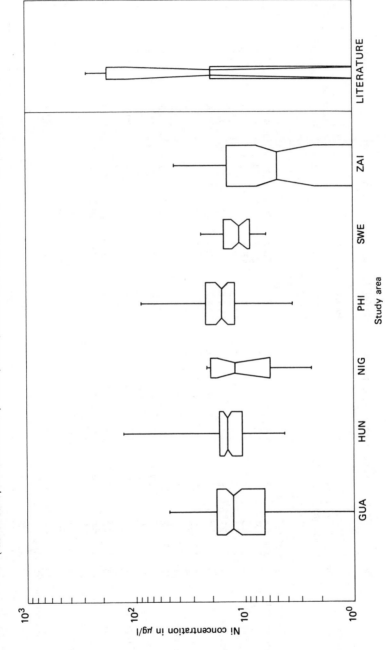

Fig. 18.   Box plots showing amounts of nickel (Ni) (μg/l original milk) in human milk specimens from six study areas
(identified by 3-letter country codes); comparison with data from the scientific literature (13)

Table 21. Statistical summary of amounts of nickel found in human milk (µg/l original milk)

Study area	Study group	No. of observations	Minimum[a]	Percentiles							Maximum	SD (median)	
				10	16	25	50 (median)	75	84	90		absolute	relative (%)
Data from reference analytical laboratory													
Guatemala	1	12	4.1	4.6	6.0	9.7	18.0	23.7	40.4	47.1	49.3	3.7	21
	2	24	0.0	0.0	1.0	7.0	13.7	21.9	27.1	34.0	49.2	2.8	20
	3	38	0.0	3.8	4.8	5.9	10.8	16.7	18.4	20.3	27.3	1.6	15
	All	74	0.0	3.4	4.7	6.6	12.9	18.3	22.8	27.1	49.3	1.3	10
Hungary	1	21	8.7	9.7	11.3	12.7	14.6	16.8	19.5	25.4	26.6	0.8	6
	2	29	4.3	5.4	6.8	8.0	14.2	18.6	24.3	32.9	129.6	1.8	13
	3	20	4.4	8.4	9.1	9.6	13.8	17.8	21.8	26.3	30.6	1.7	12
	All	70	4.3	7.6	8.8	10.5	14.4	17.0	22.3	26.6	129.6	0.7	5
Nigeria	1	5	4.5	4.5	4.5	5.5	8.3	21.1	22.0	22.0	22.0	6.4	78
	2	1	21.5	21.5	21.5	21.5	21.5	21.5	21.5	21.5	21.5	0.0	0
	3	8	2.4	2.4	3.5	5.2	12.2	14.1	18.3	21.2	21.2	2.9	24
	All	14	2.4	3.4	4.6	5.8	12.2	20.4	21.4	21.7	22.0	3.6	30
Philippines	1	14	3.6	4.7	6.3	7.3	15.6	20.8	22.3	23.7	24.4	3.3	21
	2	28	5.9	9.9	11.0	13.6	16.2	27.2	34.2	38.5	87.0	2.4	15
	3	20	6.2	10.2	11.2	12.1	16.1	22.2	23.3	30.5	51.2	2.1	13
	All	62	3.6	7.4	10.4	12.2	16.1	22.6	26.5	33.2	87.0	1.2	8
Sweden	All	31	6.3	6.9	7.2	8.8	11.0	15.4	17.5	19.8	24.5	1.1	10
Zaire	1	34	0.0	0.0	0.0	2.3	7.1	14.7	23.1	28.3	43.8	2.0	28
	3	25	0.0	0.0	0.0	0.0	4.9	14.5	26.6	32.7	37.8	2.7	54
	All	59	0.0	0.0	0.0	0.0	4.9	14.2	26.6	29.0	43.8	1.7	35
Data from the literature													
	All	5	20.0	20.0	20.0	20.0	20.0	179.5	276.0	276.0	276.0	66.1	330

[a] Zeros indicate values below the detection limit (~2 µg/l).

Phosphorus

Light absorption spectrometry (spectrophotometry) was used as the reference analytical method for phosphorus (see Annex 9). The quality assurance data obtained during the course of the project confirmed that this method had satisfactory accuracy and precision. The results obtained are presented in Table 22 and Fig. 19.

Differences between study areas

Most of the values reported were in the relatively narrow range of 120–180 mg/1. Although some differences were observed (e.g., Guatemala and Hungary), their magnitudes were not very large.

Other significant findings

There were none

Other data

Four collection centres provided data: Hungary, the Philippines, and Sweden (Table 22), and Zaire (urban: 182 ± 10 mg/1;[a] rural: 177 ± 12 mg/1[a]). Satisfactory agreement with the results from the reference laboratory was observed.

---

[a] Mean $\pm$ SD for specimens collected 3 months after birth.

Table 22. Statistical summary of amounts of phosphorus found in human milk (mg/l original milk)

Study area	Study group	No. of observations	Minimum	Percentiles							Maximum	SD (median)	
				10	16	25	50 median	75	84	90		absolute	relative (%)
Data from reference analytical laboratory													
Guatemala	1	7	129	129	132	141	148	157	158	159	159	6	4
	2	8	149	149	156	165	174	192	196	198	198	9	5
	3	11	126	127	129	139	147	157	157	163	164	5	3
	All	26	126	129	140	144	154	165	176	190	198	4	3
Hungary	1	5	108	108	108	112	127	143	158	158	158	13	10
	2	15	95	116	129	132	139	146	158	172	182	3	2
	3	6	119	119	119	123	127	146	167	172	172	9	7
	All	26	95	113	120	127	136	143	157	167	182	3	2
Nigeria	1	1	127	127	127	127	127	127	127	127	127	0	0
	3	2	146	146	146	146	161	177	177	177	177	20	12
	All	3	127	127	127	146	146	177	177	177	177	26	18
Philippines	1	1	144	144	144	144	144	144	144	144	144	0	0
	2	9	129	129	132	135	143	163	167	168	168	9	6
	3	5	137	137	137	151	317	352	357	357	357	83	26
	All	15	129	132	135	137	147	168	331	351	357	8	5
Sweden	All	4	131	131	131	133	142	149	150	150	150	7	5
Zaire	1	20	108	118	120	126	153	175	175	175	150	10	7
	3	13	86	104	133	143	164	192	201	313	385	12	8
	All	33	86	118	123	135	155	175	184	200	385	7	4

Data from collection centres (for their own samples)

Hungary	1	23	104	112	116	126	141	169	179	191	197	8	6
	2	56	95	107	121	131	151	166	197	220	332	4	3
	3	28	85	121	127	133	161	186	198	207	258	9	6
	All	107	85	115	121	129	150	172	194	199	332	4	3
Philippines	1	18	88	94	97	101	116	129	130	131	135	6	5
	2	29	81	99	104	108	118	124	131	138	158	3	2
	3	27	79	90	96	105	115	126	135	144	151	4	3
	All	74	79	95	99	105	117	126	130	136	158	2	2
Sweden	All	28	99	109	112	124	134	143	149	156	163	3	3

Data from the literature

	All	17	95	108	116	127	142	151	152	157	160	5	4

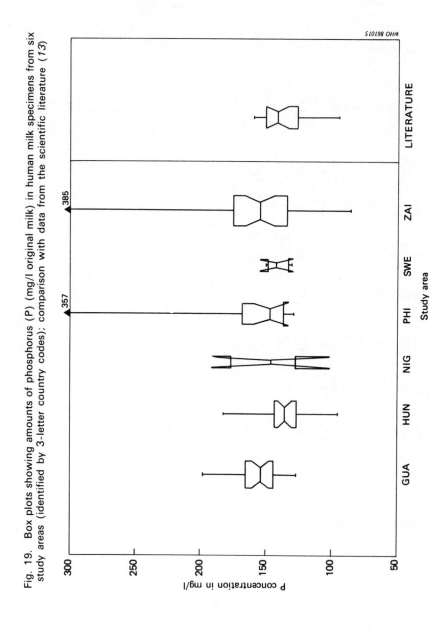

Fig. 19. Box plots showing amounts of phosphorus (P) (mg/l original milk) in human milk specimens from six study areas (identified by 3-letter country codes); comparison with data from the scientific literature (13)

Potassium

Flame atomic absorption spectrometry was used as the reference analytical method for potassium (see Annex 3). The quality assurance data obtained during the course of the study confirmed that this method was working with satisfactory accuracy and precision. The results obtained are presented in Table 23 and Fig. 20.

Differences between study areas

Several significant differences were observed, the Hungarian and Swedish values being relatively high. The Nigerian values were, on the whole, relatively low, but covered a very wide range. In numerical terms the differences between the median values for the various study areas were not large.

Other significant findings

In Guatemala, the rural group had significantly lower values than either of the urban groups. Also in Guatemala, specimens collected during the first trimester had significantly higher potassium concentrations on average (and also showed more variation) than specimens collected at other times of the year.

Other data

Four collection centres provided data: Hungary, the Philippines, and Sweden (see Table 23) and Zaire (urban: 494 ± 36 mg/1;[a] rural: 611 ± 62 mg/1[a]). For specimens from Zaire, there was relatively good agreement with the reference laboratory. In all other cases, the reference laboratory reported somewhat higher values than the collection centres, presumably for analytical reasons.

---

[a] Mean $\pm$ SD for specimens collected 3 months after birth.

Table 23. Statistical summary of amounts of potassium found in human milk (mg/l original milk)

Study area	Study group	No. of observations	Minimum	Percentiles							Maximum	SD (median)	
				10	16	25	50 median	75	84	90		absolute	relative (%)
Data from reference analytical laboratory													
Guatemala	1	22	426	439	461	502	539	582	618	637	664	16	3
	2	22	216	441	462	473	508	559	576	589	733	17	3
	3	37	287	372	375	385	443	475	493	506	537	14	3
	All	81	216	378	403	437	487	533	556	578	733	10	2
Hungary	1	21	476	498	505	538	565	612	614	640	708	15	3
	2	29	422	486	514	533	546	620	637	697	785	15	3
	3	21	411	480	493	516	542	605	621	643	651	18	3
	All	71	411	487	504	529	554	609	631	644	785	9	2
Nigeria	1	5	321	321	321	361	404	602	713	713	713	100	25
	2	1	410	410	410	410	410	410	410	410	410	0	0
	3	9	234	234	292	340	509	538	560	576	576	61	12
	All	15	234	286	326	349	410	526	561	631	713	42	10
Philippines	1	16	356	379	400	417	459	541	592	645	706	29	6
	2	28	288	370	388	401	464	510	524	568	688	19	4
	3	21	333	402	427	434	469	514	560	571	600	16	3
	All	65	288	388	399	425	469	517	546	576	706	11	2
Sweden	All	29	397	466	474	476	548	587	619	627	711	19	3
Zaire	1	37	342	424	434	455	494	538	556	588	636	13	3
	3	32	404	436	466	482	534	590	616	684	1040	18	3
	All	69	342	428	441	467	511	559	591	609	1040	10	2

Data from collection centres (for their own samples)

Hungary	1	21	330	332	345	355	410	440	440	448	470	17	4
	2	34	250	355	366	377	440	460	486	535	620	13	3
	3	28	230	324	353	365	410	457	487	521	540	16	4
	All	83	230	340	360	370	420	450	466	506	620	8	2
Philippines	1	19	236	250	274	290	350	400	472	510	550	23	7
	2	29	200	250	250	275	326	360	360	360	436	15	4
	3	27	144	233	245	290	326	380	390	407	440	16	5
	All	75	144	250	251	290	326	360	380	402	550	7	2
Sweden	All	28	276	315	329	347	399	450	454	483	498	18	5

Data from the literature

	All	18	326	329	386	336	511	592	611	635	705	45	9

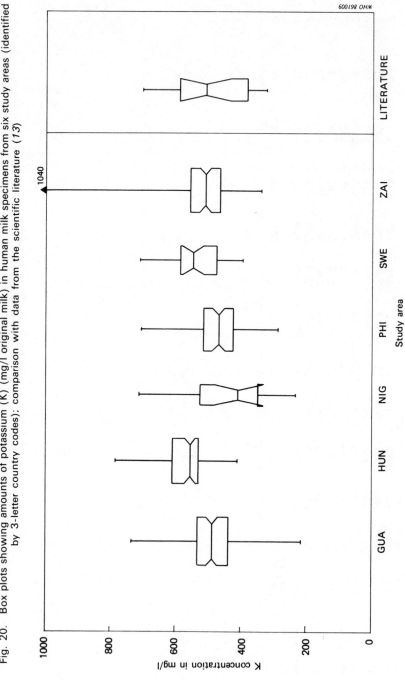

Fig. 20. Box plots showing amounts of potassium (K) (mg/l original milk) in human milk specimens from six study areas (identified by 3-letter country codes); comparison with data from the scientific literature (13)

Selenium

Instrumental neutron activation analysis was used as the reference analytical method for selenium (see Annex 5). The quality assurance data obtained during the course of the project confirmed that this method had satisfactory accuracy and precision. The results obtained are presented in Table 24 and Fig. 21.

Differences between study areas

The median values obtained in this study varied between 13 and 33 μg/1. Some of the differences were highly significant, the Philippine values being relatively high and the Hungarian and Swedish values relatively low.

Other significant findings

In Guatemala, samples collected during the first trimester contained significantly higher selenium concentrations than those collected at other times of the year. Also in Guatemala, samples collected from the rural study group had significantly lower concentrations than samples collected from either of the urban groups.

Table 24. Statistical summary of amounts of selenium found in human milk (µg/l original milk)

Study area	Study group	No. of observations	Minimum	Percentiles							Maximum	SD (median)	
				10	16	25	50 median	75	84	90		absolute	relative (%)
Data from reference analytical laboratory													
Guatemala	1	21	14.0	15.9	17.2	18.2	23.1	26.5	28.3	30.8	35.4	1.7	7
	2	24	17.6	18.6	19.5	21.1	26.7	31.3	33.1	40.8	46.2	1.9	7
	3	39	3.4	8.8	9.3	9.9	12.8	16.6	19.3	19.9	25.9	1.0	8
	All	84	3.4	9.6	10.9	12.9	19.2	25.3	28.4	31.1	46.2	1.2	7
Hungary	1	21	12.2	12.9	13.1	13.6	14.4	16.5	20.9	21.3	22.9	0.6	4
	2	29	8.8	11.0	12.3	12.4	13.9	16.3	17.2	17.4	21.5	0.7	5
	3	21	7.9	9.0	9.1	10.4	12.6	14.9	15.4	16.0	17.9	0.9	7
	All	71	7.9	10.2	11.6	12.4	13.9	15.6	17.0	17.8	22.9	0.4	3
Nigeria	1	6	16.4	16.4	16.5	17.0	21.7	28.9	36.7	38.2	38.2	4.5	21
	2	2	21.6	21.6	21.6	21.6	32.8	44.0	44.0	44.0	44.0	14.7	45
	3	10	17.9	18.0	18.6	20.4	24.7	30.7	35.5	36.4	36.5	3.0	12
	All	18	16.4	17.1	17.9	19.6	24.2	30.7	36.4	38.8	44.0	2.4	10
Philippines	1	16	22.2	23.6	24.6	28.8	35.9	43.3	45.5	48.8	54.2	3.3	9
	2	28	19.2	23.4	27.5	30.2	35.0	39.7	46.2	50.7	56.9	1.7	5
	3	21	17.4	19.8	20.4	22.2	28.5	37.7	41.2	43.1	45.1	3.1	11
	All	65	17.4	21.1	23.7	27.6	33.2	39.7	43.6	45.7	56.9	1.4	4
Sweden	All	32	3.7	8.2	9.6	11.5	13.1	17.1	19.1	21.5	24.8	0.9	7
Zaire	1	37	10.4	14.3	14.9	18.1	20.5	26.7	27.9	29.3	37.1	1.3	6
	3	32	7.9	9.4	10.7	12.5	16.8	21.4	25.6	31.5	65.8	1.5	9
	All	69	7.9	10.9	12.9	15.1	19.3	25.0	27.3	29.0	65.8	1.1	6
Data from the literature													
	All	10	9.8	10.1	12.5	13.8	19.0	22.7	32.4	44.6	46.5	2.6	14

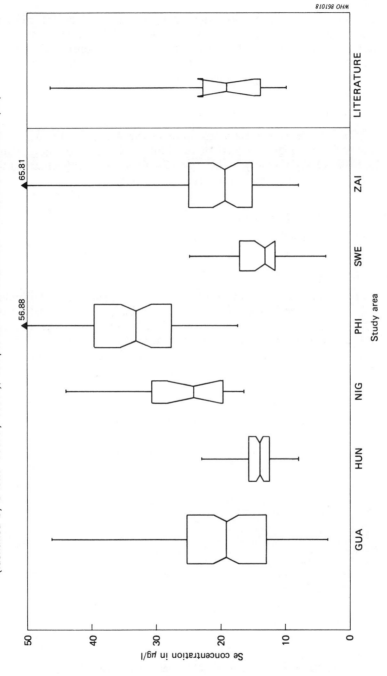

Fig. 21. Box plots showing amounts of selenium (Se) (μg/l original milk) in human milk specimens from six study areas (identified by 3-letter country codes); comparison with data from the scientific literature (13)

Sodium

Flame atomic absorption spectrometry was used as the reference analytical method for sodium (see Annex 3). The quality assurance data obtained during the course of the study confirmed that this method was working with satisfactory accuracy and precison. The results obtained are presented in Table 25 and Fig. 22.

Differences between study areas

Most of the values reported were in the range 60–170 mg/1. The values for samples collected in the Philippines (and possibly also in Zaire) were significantly higher than for most other collection centres, but the differences were numerically not very large.

Other significant findings

There were none.

Other data

Four collection centres provided data: Hungary, the Philippines, and Sweden (see Table 25), and Zaire (urban: 133 ± 12 mg/1;[a] rural: 168 ± 18 mg/1[a]. The agreement with the results from the reference laboratory was poorer than expected, and in most cases the reference laboratory obtained lower results than did the collection centres themselves.

---

[a] Mean $\pm$ SD for specimens collected 3 months after birth.

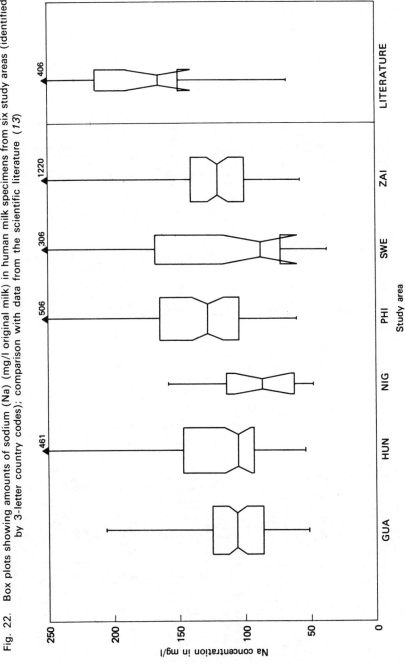

Fig. 22. Box plots showing amounts of sodium (Na) (mg/l original milk) in human milk specimens from six study areas (identified by 3-letter country codes); comparison with data from the scientific literature (13)

Table 25. Statistical summary of amounts of sodium found in human milk (mg/l original milk)

Study area	Study group	No. of observations	Minimum	Percentiles							Maximum	SD (median)	
				10	16	25	50 median	75	84	90		absolute	relative (%)
Data from reference analytical laboratory													
Guatemala	1	22	53	69	76	94	111	135	152	167	171	8	7
	2	22	51	56	67	78	100	156	176	192	206	15	15
	3	37	61	74	80	89	101	115	127	137	158	4	4
	All	81	51	67	77	86	106	125	141	163	206	4	4
Hungary	1	21	58	66	87	90	122	157	174	180	231	13	11
	2	29	70	76	87	93	104	131	148	157	221	6	6
	3	21	54	62	88	94	103	156	185	312	461	12	12
	All	71	54	77	88	93	105	147	160	178	461	6	6
Nigeria	1	5	48	48	48	55	76	155	158	158	158	42	55
	2	1	96	96	96	96	96	96	96	96	96	0	0
	3	9	48	48	53	64	87	114	116	119	119	15	18
	All	15	48	48	53	62	87	114	134	154	158	13	14
Philippines	1	16	91	98	112	118	137	207	233	258	301	21	15
	2	28	60	79	92	107	134	166	188	206	506	10	8
	3	21	69	79	85	95	118	139	150	160	170	9	8
	All	65	60	85	94	104	128	165	186	205	506	7	5
Sweden	All	29	37	55	66	72	88	168	180	196	306	17	19
Zaire	1	37	57	76	86	94	122	144	181	265	356	8	6
	3	32	85	90	96	106	120	133	196	740	1220	4	4
	All	69	57	85	92	100	120	141	183	334	1220	5	4

Data from collection centres (for their own samples)

Hungary	1	20	110	112	130	150	190	210	220	265	270	12	7
	2	34	60	85	102	137	165	210	260	315	430	12	7
	3	28	100	120	130	140	190	247	250	311	510	19	10
	All	82	60	110	130	140	180	220	250	270	510	8	5
Philippines	1	19	135	145	155	190	220	282	305	320	320	20	9
	2	29	66	115	124	146	216	233	265	326	340	15	7
	3	27	68	96	108	132	166	196	227	236	336	11	7
	All	75	66	114	132	148	190	230	257	298	340	9	5
Sweden	All	28	51	53	58	61	71	89	95	101	132	5	7
Data from the literature													
	All	16	67	70	118	150	165	213	235	288	406	15	9

Tin

Radiochemical neutron activation analysis was used as the reference analytical method for tin (see Annex 7). Despite the fact that this is a difficult element to measure reliably at the concentrations found in human milk, and that no entirely appropriate certified reference materials for it were available, there are reasonable grounds for confidence in the analytical method used in this study. However, because of difficulties in obtaining access to a suitable high-flux nuclear reactor, as well as the fact that a sample of at least 300 mg of dried milk was required for each analysis, it was only possible to analyse a very small number of milk samples, which happened to be those from Guatemala and Zaire. The results obtained are presented in Table 26 and Fig. 23.

Differences between study areas

There is no significant difference between the respective medians for Guatemala and Zaire, though it may be of interest to note that the Guatemalan data covered a much wider range of values than did the Zairian data.

Other significant findings

There were none.

Table 26. Statistical summary of amounts of tin found in human milk (µg/l original milk)

Study area	Study group	No. of obser- vations	Minimum	Percentiles							Maximum	SD (median)	
				10	16	25	50 median	75	84	90		absolute	relative (%)
Data from reference analytical laboratory													
Guatemala	1	1	2.29	2.29	2.29	2.29	2.29	2.29	2.29	2.29	2.29	0.00	0
	3	3	2.19	2.19	2.19	2.19	2.39	10.28	10.28	10.28	10.28	4.33	181
	All	4	2.19	2.19	2.19	2.22	2.34	8.31	10.28	10.28	10.28	2.82	120
Zaire	1	4	0.60	0.60	0.60	0.64	1.00	1.27	1.28	1.28	1.28	0.29	30
	3	4	1.13	1.13	1.13	1.21	1.52	1.63	1.64	1.64	1.64	0.20	13
	All	8	0.60	0.60	0.66	0.84	1.26	1.57	1.63	1.64	1.64	0.24	19

Fig. 23. Box plots showing amounts of tin (Sn) (μg/l original milk) in human milk specimens from two study areas (identified by 3-letter country codes)

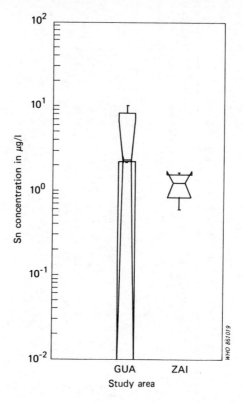

Vanadium

Radiochemical neutron activation analysis was used as the reference analytical method for vanadium (see Annex 7). Despite the fact that this is a difficult element to measure reliably at the concentrations found in human milk, and that no entirely appropriate certified reference materials for it were available, there are reasonable grounds for confidence in the analytical method used in this study. The results obtained are presented in Table 27 and Fig. 24.

Differences between study areas

Several significant differences are apparent in the data. Samples collected in the Philippines and Nigeria had relatively high values as compared with Sweden and Hungary, which had relatively low ones.

Other significant findings

In Sweden, samples collected during the first trimester had significantly lower vanadium concentrations than did samples collected during the fourth trimester. In Zaire, samples collected from urban mothers had significantly lower concentrations than did samples collected from rural mothers, and it is this difference, amounting to a factor of about 5.7 between the respective median values, that accounts for the large scatter in the results when both groups are combined.

Table 27. Statistical summary of amounts of vanadium found in human milk (µg/l original milk)

Study area	Study group	No. of observations	Minimum	Percentiles							Maximum	SD (median)	
				10	16	25	50 median	75	84	90		absolute	relative (%)
Data from reference analytical laboratory													
Guatemala	1	8	0.09	0.09	0.11	0.14	0.17	0.31	0.37	0.42	0.42	0.05	33
	2	8	0.16	0.16	0.17	0.18	0.34	0.52	0.53	0.53	0.53	0.11	34
	3	10	0.10	0.10	0.12	0.14	0.20	0.35	0.68	1.20	1.28	0.06	30
	All	26	0.09	0.11	0.14	0.15	0.21	0.41	0.49	0.53	1.28	0.05	22
Hungary	1	6	0.09	0.09	0.10	0.11	0.13	0.18	0.22	0.23	0.23	0.03	20
	2	7	0.04	0.04	0.05	0.08	0.09	0.12	0.13	0.14	0.14	0.01	15
	3	6	0.08	0.08	0.08	0.09	0.11	0.26	0.33	0.34	0.34	0.07	61
	All	19	0.04	0.08	0.08	0.09	0.11	0.15	0.22	0.23	0.34	0.01	11
Nigeria	1	3	0.31	0.31	0.31	0.31	0.58	0.69	0.69	0.69	0.69	0.21	36
	3	3	0.29	0.29	0.29	0.29	0.35	0.58	0.58	0.58	0.58	0.15	44
	All	6	0.29	0.29	0.29	0.30	0.46	0.61	0.68	0.69	0.69	0.11	25
Philippines	1	5	0.51	0.51	0.51	0.61	0.75	2.41	3.86	3.86	3.86	0.75	99
	2	5	0.54	0.54	0.54	0.55	0.68	0.84	0.96	0.96	0.96	0.12	18
	3	4	0.30	0.30	0.30	0.31	0.48	0.71	0.74	0.74	0.74	0.19	39
	All	14	0.30	0.32	0.41	0.53	0.69	0.80	0.96	2.41	3.86	0.07	10
Sweden	All	8	0.05	0.05	0.06	0.07	0.13	0.14	0.15	0.16	0.16	0.02	18
Zaire	1	10	0.09	0.09	0.10	0.11	0.13	0.23	0.89	2.58	2.84	0.03	25
	3	10	0.07	0.09	0.22	0.30	0.74	1.17	1.98	2.51	2.59	0.26	35
	All	20	0.07	0.09	0.10	0.12	0.27	0.94	1.49	2.51	2.84	0.17	64
Data from the literature													
	All	4	0.10	0.10	0.10	0.82	4.00	5.00	5.00	5.00	5.00	1.93	48

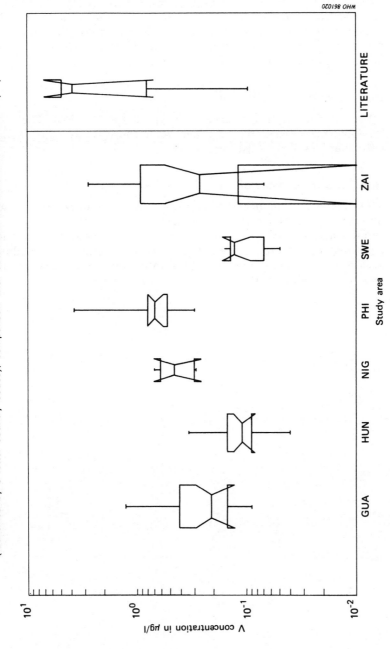

Fig. 24. Box plots showing amounts of vanadium (V) (µg/l original milk) in human milk specimens from six study areas (identified by 3-letter country codes); comparison with data from the scientific literature (13)

Zinc

Instrumental neutron activation analysis was used as the reference analytical method for zinc (see Annex 5). The quality assurance data obtained during the course of the study confirmed that, as far as could be judged, this method was working reliably. The results obtained are presented in Table 28 and Fig. 25.

Differences between study areas

Several significant differences are apparent in the data. The values for Guatemala were relatively high while those for Hungary and, in particular, Sweden, were low.

Other significant findings

In Guatemala, the urban elite group showed the lowest values, with the urban poor and rural groups having values higher by factors of about 2 and 4 respectively. Also in Guatemala, significant differences were observed according to the time of year. Samples collected during the fourth trimester contained significantly higher zinc concentrations than those collected at other times of the year.

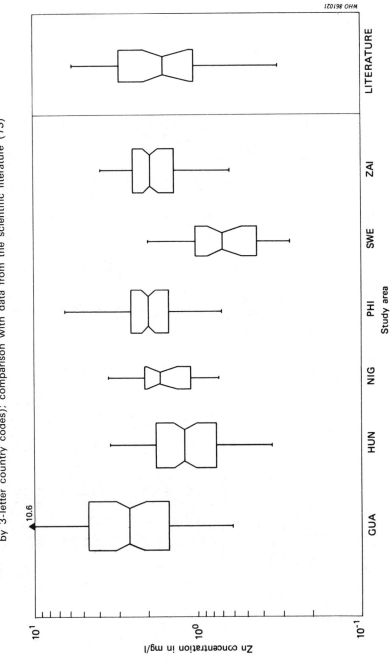

Fig. 25. Box plots showing amounts of zinc (Zn) (mg/l original milk) in human milk specimens from six study areas (identified by 3-letter country codes); comparison with data from the scientific literature (13)

WHO 861021

Table 28. Statistical summary of amounts of zinc found in human milk (mg/l original milk)

Study area	Study group	No. of observations	Minimum	Percentiles							Maximum	SD (median)	
				10	16	25	50 median	75	84	90		absolute	relative (%)
Data from reference analytical laboratory													
Guatemala	1	21	0.61	0.67	0.72	0.82	1.17	1.94	2.09	2.55	3.00	0.23	19
	2	24	0.67	1.10	1.30	1.49	2.07	2.69	2.94	3.31	3.71	0.23	11
	3	39	1.28	1.85	2.62	3.04	4.93	6.98	7.93	8.37	10.60	0.58	12
	All	84	0.61	0.96	1.16	1.49	2.61	4.64	6.20	7.47	10.60	0.32	12
Hungary	1	21	0.56	0.64	0.74	0.88	1.20	1.91	2.42	2.96	3.41	0.21	17
	2	29	0.35	0.52	0.54	0.62	1.07	1.86	1.94	1.99	2.52	0.21	20
	3	21	0.48	0.55	0.59	0.80	1.39	1.73	2.15	2.63	3.31	0.19	14
	All	71	0.35	0.55	0.60	0.77	1.20	1.79	2.01	2.28	3.41	0.11	9
Nigeria	1	6	0.81	0.81	0.84	0.97	1.23	2.12	2.66	2.77	2.77	0.43	35
	2	2	1.25	1.25	1.25	1.25	1.63	2.00	2.00	2.00	2.00	0.49	30
	3	10	0.74	0.78	1.00	1.21	1.86	2.58	3.46	3.49	3.50	0.40	22
	All	18	0.74	0.81	1.02	1.10	1.68	2.09	2.75	3.45	3.50	0.22	13
Philippines	1	16	1.22	1.32	1.38	1.49	2.08	2.68	2.78	3.96	6.38	0.28	13
	2	28	0.71	1.01	1.22	1.65	2.04	2.59	2.98	3.45	4.71	0.17	8
	3	21	0.91	1.02	1.24	1.42	1.87	2.35	2.62	3.03	3.43	0.19	10
	All	65	0.71	1.18	1.33	1.49	1.98	2.52	2.74	3.16	6.38	0.12	6
Sweden	All	32	0.27	0.31	0.38	0.43	0.70	1.03	1.06	1.45	1.99	0.10	14
Zaire	1	37	0.88	1.26	1.32	1.51	2.16	2.75	2.82	3.42	3.87	0.19	9
	3	32	0.63	0.77	0.89	1.07	1.68	2.34	2.45	2.56	2.90	0.21	12
	All	69	0.63	0.92	1.11	1.38	1.92	2.45	2.71	2.82	3.87	0.12	6

Data from collection centres (for their own samples)

Hungary	1	18	0.85	0.94	0.98	1.30	1.45	1.61	1.73	2.09	2.95	0.07	5
	2	31	0.54	0.70	0.72	0.84	1.14	1.60	1.83	1.95	2.05	0.13	11
	3	21	0.43	0.52	0.63	0.93	1.22	2.06	2.48	2.65	3.26	0.23	19
	All	70	0.43	0.69	0.82	0.93	1.26	1.65	1.99	2.05	3.26	0.08	6
Philippines	1	19	1.80	1.80	1.84	2.00	2.75	3.50	4.10	4.75	5.05	0.32	12
	2	29	1.63	1.70	1.96	2.10	2.50	3.05	3.40	4.00	4.20	0.16	7
	3	27	1.63	1.65	1.80	1.80	2.35	3.00	3.25	3.54	4.90	0.21	9
	All	75	1.63	1.80	1.80	2.00	2.50	3.10	3.50	3.88	5.05	0.12	5
Sweden	All	28	0.37	0.43	0.49	0.61	0.76	0.91	0.99	1.17	1.33	0.05	7

Data from the literature

	All	35	0.32	0.61	0.68	1.04	1.60	2.95	3.21	3.69	5.77	0.30	19

4. Discussion

Comparison between results of this study and data from the literature

Antimony

There is almost no information on this element in the literature (*13*). A recent study (*16*) produced significantly lower values for milk from Yugoslav mothers, namely 0.16 ± 0.17 (4) $\mu g/l^a$, range $0.06-0.43$ $\mu g/l$. Clearly, further work is required to establish well validated values for antimony in human milk.

Arsenic

There is very little information on arsenic in the scientific literature with which to compare the findings of this study. Owing to difficulties in determining this element reliably in biological materials (*8*), any values reported need to be interpreted with extreme caution. Data reported in the literature vary from 3.20 to 36 $\mu g/l$. Results from this study are all on the low side (median value below 2 $\mu g/l$) except for the Philippines where the median value was around 19 $\mu g/l$. Three recent studies conducted under the auspices of IAEA, with similar analytical quality control procedures to those described in this report, lend further support to the values reported in Table 6. Dang et al. (*15*) found 0.41 ± 0.12 (7) $\mu g/l^a$ in mature milk from well-nourished Indian subjects. Kosta et al. (*16*) found very similar values in milk samples from Yugoslav mothers, namely 0.44 ± 0.23 (5) $\mu g/l^a$, range 0.09–0.73 $\mu g/l$. Values found by Cortes-Toro (*17*) in northern Chile, were somewhat higher, namely 3.04 ± 0.96 (11) $\mu g/l^a$, range 1.6–4.8 $\mu g/l$, in a region with high natural concentrations of arsenic in drinking water. In contrast, in the Santiago region of Chile, the values were less than 0.1 $\mu g/l$.

Cadmium

There is little information on cadmium in the scientific literature and the published data vary widely, from 0.10 to 19.0 $\mu g/l$. In a recent study (*16*) on Yugoslav subjects, conducted under the auspices of

---

[a] Mean $\pm$ SD (no. of measurements), values for mature milk.

IAEA, with similar analytical quality assurance procedures to those described in this report, the result, namely <0.3 μg/l in mature milk, was consistent with results reported in Table 7.

Calcium

There is good agreement between the findings of this study and data reported in the scientific literature (13).

Chlorine

The values for chlorine found in this study, although of the same magnitude as comparable data reported by other workers, were nevertheless significantly lower (by 10–20%). Because of the attention given to the reliability of the method used and the quality assurance in this study, it is reasonable to have more confidence in these findings than in previously reported data.

Chromium

The reliable determination of this element at the low levels present in biological materials is difficult (8, 19) and consequently there is little published information on its concentration in breast milk. The fact that the values obtained during this study are all lower than the data cited by Iyengar (13) (and also lower than the results reported by the Hungarian collection centre) is not, in itself, a cause for concern. Further evidence in support of the proposition that normal levels of chromium in human milk are lower than previously reported is provided by Kumpulainen et al. (20), and Casey & Hambidge (21). The former group measured a value of 0.49 ± 0.07 (8) μg/l[a] for a pooled sample of milk from Finnish subjects. The latter workers reported a mean concentration of 0.30 ± 0.17 (255) μg/l[a] for breast milk from American mothers at various stages of lactation. These new sets of values, both obtained by graphite furnace atomic absorption spectrometry, are thus even lower than the values reported in Table 10, and raise some doubts as to whether these latter data might not have been distorted by a systematic analytical error or even by contamination. The analytical quality assurance data reported in Annex 3 argue against the existence of such errors, but since the analytical precision was so poor, the question cannot at this stage be completely resolved. The data obtained from this study should, therefore, be interpreted with caution. If any conclusion is to be drawn it is that actual chromium concentrations in human milk are probably equal to or less than the values obtained in this study.

---

[a] Mean $\pm$ SD (no. of measurements), values for mature milk.

Cobalt

There is very little information on cobalt in the scientific literature with which to compare the findings of this study. Owing to difficulties in determining this element reliably at low levels in biological materials (8), any values reported need to be interpreted with extreme caution. Values reported in the literature range between 1 and 8.6 µg/l. Three recent studies conducted under the auspices of IAEA, with similar analytical quality assurance procedures to those described in this report, lend further support to the values reported in Table 11. Dang et al. (18) found values of around 0.5µg/l in mature milk from 14 Indian subjects. Cortes-Toro (17) found similar values in the Santiago region of Chile, namely 0.37 ± 0.22 (16) µg/l[a], range 0.03–0.77 µg/l. Kosta et al. (16) observed somewhat lower values of about 0.1 µg/l in colostrum and transitional milk specimens from Yugoslav subjects.

Copper

In general, the findings of the study are in agreement with values from the literature, as cited by Iyengar (13). Three recent studies conducted under the auspices of IAEA lend further support to the values reported in Table 12. Dang et al. (15) found 340 ± 80 (7) µg/l[a] in mature milk from well-nourished Indian subjects. Kosta et al. (16) found 253 ± 52 (7) µg/l[a] in mature milk from Yugoslav subjects. Cortes-Toro (17) found 249 ± 54 (12) µg/l[a], range 139–333 µg/l in the Santiago region of Chile, 397 ± 105 (12) µg/l[a], range 210–629 µg/l in the northern region (in which there are copper mining activities). These data are consistent with results reported from other studies where variations between different geographical areas were observed. Values as high as 500 µg/l have been reported from India (22).

Fluorine

The results indicated that there were great variations between countries, the median concentrations ranging from 6.8 to 117.7 µg/l. Most values, however, were below 25 µg/l, and comparable to those reported by Esala et al. (23) for milk specimens from Finnish mothers, namely 5.0 and 8.9 µg/l (median values) for subjects living respectively in low and high fluorine areas, and by Backer et al. (24) in the Netherlands. Exceptionally high values were recorded in the Philippines. The geochemical environment strongly influences the fluorine content of foods grown in any one area, which presumably explains the wide difference in fluorine concentrations observed in human milk in this study.

---

[a] Mean ± SD (no. of measurements), values for mature milk.

Iodine

The results were remarkably similar in all countries (except Zaire, where the concentration, 15 μg/l, was low) and were close to the usually quoted level of 50 μg/l, range 40–80 μg/l (*27, 28*). In Zaire, the study was conducted in the Kivu province which is notorious for its endemic goitre and low iodine intake: the latter is reflected in the low iodine values found in breast milk. One recent study conducted under the auspices of IAEA, which used similar analytical quality control procedures to those described in this report, lends further support to the values reported in Table 14. Kosta et al. (*16*) found 88±83 (6) μg/l[a] in mature milk from Yugoslav subjects. Much higher levels, 150 μg/l (mode), range 80–7000 μg/l, have been reported in human milk specimens from Japanese subjects who consume dietary algae (*29*).

Iron

Concentrations in this study ranged between 346 and 720 μg/l indicating some, but not large, differences between the various areas investigated. This is consistent with reports from the literature which show a range of 200–1300 μg/l (*13*). Some differences between rural and urban groups were observed although no definite trend could be detected. In Zaire, the rural group, in which the mothers and children showed signs of malnutrition, had a higher concentration of iron (851 μg/l) than the urban group (388 μg/l). In this study, iron concentration in breast milk appeared to be unrelated to the iron status or to the socioeconomic status of the mother, which is consistent with other reports in the literature (*25, 26*).

Lead

Although the values found in Hungary, the Philippines and Sweden were higher than those in Guatemala, Nigeria and Zaire, they are nevertheless in reasonably good agreement with data reported in the scientific literature (*13*).

Magnesium

The findings of this study are in good agreement with data reported in the literature (*13*).

Manganese

Concentrations of 4 μg/l in mid-lactation (2–6 months) and 6–8 μg/l in late lactation have been reported by Vuori (*30*) and Vaughan et al.

---

[a] Mean±SD (no. of measurements), values for mature milk.

(*31*). These values compare well with those found in this study in Guatemala, Hungary and Sweden. More recently, Dang et al. (*15*) found 23.0 ± 8.3 (7) $\mu g/l^a$ in mature milk from Indian subjects. Kosta et al. (*16*) found somewhat lower values for mature milk samples collected in Yugoslavia, namely 3.3 ± 2.1 (4) $\mu g/l.^a$

Mercury

The findings of this study are in general agreement with the data cited by Iyengar (*13*). Broadly similar data, but at the lower end of the range, have recently been reported by Kosta et al. (*16*), namely 1.0 ± 0.9 (6) $\mu g/l^a$ for mature milk samples from Yugoslav subjects. The country with the highest median value was Sweden. Fish consumption is relatively high in that country and it could be suggested that the increased mercury content of human milk may be coming from this source.

Molybdenum

Concentrations were very low and sometimes at the limit of detection in most study areas; only in the Philippines and in Nigeria were concentrations higher. There is very little information in the literature with which to compare these findings. In a recent study conducted under the auspices of IAEA, Dang et al. (*15*) found 6.4 ± 3.8 (7) $\mu g/l^a$ in mature milk from Indian subjects. Concentrations of molybdenum in food are known to vary considerably depending on the environment in which the food was grown, and this is probably the origin of the large differences in molybdenum concentration in human milk observed in this study.

Nickel

There is so little information on nickel in the literature that no meaningful comparison can be made.

Phosphorus

The findings of this study are similar to data reported in the scientific literature (*13*).

Potassium

The findings of this study are in good agreement with data reported in the scientific literature (*13*).

---

[a] Mean $\pm$ SD (no. of measurements), values for mature milk.

Selenium

Selenium is one of the few trace elements that can generally be determined in biological materials with reasonably good reliability (*8*). It is therefore not surprising that the results of this study agree well with the data reported in the scientific literature (*13*). Three recent studies conducted under the auspices of IAEA, with similar analytical quality control procedures to those described in this report, lend further support to the values reported in Table 24. Dang et al. (*18*) found values of around 20 µg/l in mature milk from Indian mothers. Cortes et al. (*17*) found 20.0±3.9 (14) µg/l[a], range 14.6–26.6 µg/l in milk samples collected in the Santiago area of Chile. Somewhat lower values of 8.5±1.9 (6) µg/l[a], range 6.6–11.9 µg/l were reported by Kosta et al. (*16*) in milk from Yugoslav mothers. Selenium levels in foodstuffs are known to vary widely according to the geochemical environment in which the foodstuffs are grown, and this presumably explains the variability observed in this study.

Sodium

The results reported by the reference laboratory are lower than those reported by the collection centres and most of the data reported in the literature (*13*). However, the reference laboratory obtained consistent results for the quality control material A-11 milk powder. Although these results are about 7% lower than the certified value, they are still within the specified confidence interval (see Annex 3). There are thus good grounds for believing the data from the reference laboratory to be correct or, at least, not more than 7% too low.

Tin

There are practically no other data in the literature with which to compare the findings from the present study. However, Kosta et al. (*16*) who served as reference analysts in the present study, reported much lower values, namely of less than 0.3 µg/l, in four samples of mature milk collected from Yugoslav mothers.

Vanadium

There is very little information on vanadium in the scientific literature with which to compare these findings. Kosta et al. (*16*) who served as reference analysts for vanadium in this study, reported values of less than or equal to about 0.15 µg/l in mature milk collected from Yugoslav mothers.

---

[a] Mean±SD (no. of measurements), values for mature milk.

Zinc

Zinc is one of the few trace elements that can generally be determined in biological materials with reasonably good reliability (*8*). It is therefore not surprising that the results of this study agree well with data reported in the literature (*13*). Three recent studies conducted under the auspices of IAEA, with similar analytical quality control procedures to those described in this report, lend further support to the values reported in Table 28. Dang et al. (*18*) found values of 2.4 ± 1.2 (7) mg/l[a] in mature milk from Indian mothers. Cortes-Toro (*17*) found significantly higher values, namely 3.6 ± 1.0 (16) mg/l[a], range 2.0–5.4 mg/l, in milk samples collected in the Santiago area of Chile. Somewhat lower values of 1.44 ± 0.11 (7) mg/l[a] were reported by Kosta et al. (*16*) in milk from Yugoslav mothers.

Sources of variation in the elemental composition of human milk

The composition of human milk is by no means constant and several factors, both physiological and non-physiological, have been found to be responsible, either directly or indirectly, for the variations observed. Physiological factors include: the stage of lactation, the time of day, the time of sampling during feeding (within-feed variations), and the overall nutritional status of the mother. In addition, there may be effects caused by disease, medication and the use of hormonal contraceptives. Non-physiological factors include geochemical and other environmental aspects, as well as the impact of certain habits such as tobacco-smoking and drinking of alcohol. Detailed references to some of these factors may be found in the report on the second phase of this study (*2*) and in a review (*13*).

Variations with time after delivery

Longitudinal studies extending up to several months following delivery have provided evidence of a progressive decrease of both minor and trace elements in breast milk. With the exception of potassium, the remaining minor elements (calcium, chlorine, magnesium, nitrogen, phosphorus, sodium and sulfur) occur at very high levels in colostrum and are responsible for the high ash content of early secretions. However, their levels rapidly decrease throughout the transitional phase and remain either steady or continue to decline at a slow rate during the remainder of the lactation period. The behaviour of trace elements, as may be seen from Table 29, is somewhat variable. Some, like copper and zinc, decline significantly from the values reached during the first three months; others, like iron, may decline by only a small factor, and some, like manganese do not

---

[a] Mean $\pm$ SD (no. of measurements), values for mature milk.

Table 29. Trace mineral content of human milk at different stages of lactation[a]

Months postpartum	No. of samples	Breast-milk concentration in ppm					
		Calcium	Copper	Iron	Magnesium	Manganese	Zinc
1–3	28	257	0.43	0.49	31	0.020	1.60
4–6	39	236	0.33	0.43	37	0.024	1.05
7–9	23	175	0.31	0.42	26	0.025	0.75
10–12	13	170	0.24	0.38	29	0.018	0.63
13–18	28	180	0.28	0.38	30	0.014	0.69
19+	30	150	0.27	0.42	26	0.019	0.59

[a] Data from Vaughan et al. (31).

decline at all. Because of the design of the study, it was not possible to study the variations of minor and trace element concentrations in breast milk during the postpartum period.

Within-feed variations

These have not been included in the present study, but are known to be important. For example, in one investigation, the mean concentration of iron was reported to have risen significantly from 0.23 to 0.34 mg/l in foremilk samples (i.e., at the beginning of suckling) and from 0.25 to 0.51 mg/l in hind-milk samples (i.e., at the end of suckling) (32). This is despite the fact that, as just mentioned, iron concentrations as a whole remain reasonably constant over the entire lactation period.

Seasonal variations

Although seasonal variations have been observed in the concentrations of some trace elements, neither a systematic effect nor correlation with any particular season was observed in this study.

Socioeconomic status

Differences in the concentrations of some minor and trace elements have been observed between urban well-to-do, urban poor and rural groups but, again, no consistent trend could be identified.

Geographical variations

Geochemical influences are thought to be the main source of variability observed in this study. Table 30 summarizes some of the geographical variability in the elemental contents of human milk observed and, for comparison, Table 31 reports data on the concentrations of five trace elements in soils from Hungary, Nigeria and the Philippines. It is noteworthy that in Hungary concentrations of trace elements are generally low, both in soils and milk samples, while in the Philippines they are generally high.

Concentrations of minor and trace elements in breast milk in Hungary and Sweden are generally low compared to the other countries with the exception of those of potassium and lead which are high; concentrations of mercury are also high in Sweden. The same elements are present in high or even very high concentrations in the Philippines. This is most probably a reflection of levels present in foodstuffs, which are generally dependent on the geochemical environment in which the food is grown. For example, the consumption of foods rich in iodine can rapidly affect the

Table 30. Comparative concentrations of some minor and trace elements in breast milk in the areas covered by the study

Element	Concentration level					
	Guatemala	Hungary	Nigeria	Philippines	Sweden	Zaire
Antimony	Low	Low	—	High	—	—
Arsenic	—	—	—	High	—	—
Cadmium	—	—	High	High	Low	Low
Calcium	High	—	Low	—	Low	—
Chlorine	—	—	—	High	—	—
Chromium	—	Low	High	High	—	—
Cobalt	—	Low	High	High	—	—
Copper	High	Low	High	High	Low	Low
Fluorine	Low	—	—	—	—	Low
Iodine	Low	—	—	—	—	Low
Iron	Low	Low	—	High	High	Low
Lead	Low	High	Low	High	—	High
Magnesium	—	—	Low	Low	Low	—
Manganese	Low	Low	—	High	High	—
Mercury	—	—	—	—	High	—
Molybdenum	—	—	—	High	—	Low
Nickel	—	—	—	—	—	—
Phosphorus	—	High	—	—	High	—
Potassium	—	Low	—	High	High	—
Selenium	—	—	—	High	Low	—
Sodium	—	—	—	High	—	—
Tin	—	—	—	—	—	—
Vanadium	—	Low	High	High	Low	—
Zinc	High	Low	—	—	Low	—

Table 31. Trace element levels in soils in some countries[a]

| Country | Concentration level | | | | |
	Copper	Iron	Manganese	Molybdenum	Zinc
Hungary	low	low	low	low	low
Nigeria	normal-low	normal-low	high	normal-low	variable low to high
Philippines	exceptionally high	high	high	normal	high

[a] Data from Sillanpaa (33).

concentration of this element in breast milk. It has been shown that following consumption of certain dietary algae known to be rich in iodine (estimated intake through this source, up to 38 mg per day) during the previous 24 hours, iodine concentration in breast milk was elevated to extremely high levels, up to 7000 $\mu g/l$ (*29*). Similarly, high levels of consumption of fish can increase mercury levels in milk. High concentrations of mercury ($7.62 \pm 2.7\mu g/l$) have been reported in the milk of Eskimo mothers from coastal areas, whose diet consists predominantly of fish with a high mercury content, whereas Eskimo mothers from the interior and urban regions showed much lower levels (3.2 ± 0.8 and 3.3 ± 0.5 $\mu g/l$, respectively) (*34*).

Environmental contamination can also be a source of trace elements in human milk. For example, in an investigation involving subjects from a town with prominent lead pollution of the atmosphere, the lead concentrations in milk were found to be evaluated to 420 ± 20 $\mu g/kg$ as compared with control values of 30 $\mu g/kg$ (*35*). The same factor is probably responsible for the high values found in this study in Hungary, Sweden, and possibly the Philippines.

Daily intake of minor and trace elements from breast milk and comparison with recommended intake

Daily dietary intakes of the breast-fed infants can be calculated by multiplying the concentration of the element in the breast milk by the amount taken per day. These data are presented in Table 32 using, as multiplication factors, the *median* daily intake of milk in each of the respective study areas (see *2*). The following median values were used (grams per day): Guatemala, 636; Hungary, 670; Sweden, 800; the Philippines, 639 (this figure excludes study group A, which had a high proportion of mothers feeding breast-milk substitutes in addition to breast milk); and Zaire, 467. For Nigeria, comparable data are not available; a median intake of 642 grams per day was assumed (i.e., the mean of the median intakes at the other collection centres).

Table 32 compares these intakes with recommended daily intakes proposed by WHO (*7*) and the US National Academy of Sciences (NAS) (*36*). The figures quoted are to be interpreted as recommended dietary allowances or intakes, if a single figure is given, or estimated safe and adequate intakes, if a range is given. The table also shows the maximum tolerable intakes set by the Joint FAO/WHO Expert Committee on Food Additives (*37–41*).

Antimony

Median intakes of antimony in this study (Table 32) varied widely between 0.6 μg per day (Guatemala) and 7.0 μg per day (the

Table 32. Measured daily intakes of minor and trace elements through milk for 3-month-old babies, and comparison with WHO (7) and NAS/NRC (36) recommendations

| Element | Unit | Daily intake, median value (range)[a] | | | | | | Recommended daily allowances[b] | | Maximum tolerable daily intake (FAO/WHO)[e] |
		Guatemala	Hungary	Nigeria	Philippines	Sweden	Zaire	WHO[c]	NAS[d]	
Antimony	µg	0.6 (<0.1–1.4)	1.1 (0.5–1.9)	2.6 (0.4–11)	7.0 (2.7–14)	2.4 (1.6–6.8)	1.7 (0.8–3.8)	—	—	—
Arsenic	µg	0.18 (0.07–0.41)	0.16 (0.13–0.27)	1.1 (0.4–5.9)	12 (5–20)	0.44 (0.30–2.8)	0.12 (0.07–0.28)	—	—	12
Cadmium	µg	<0.6 (<0.6–1.2)	<0.7 (<0.7–1.2)	2.4 (<0.6–6.8)	1.7 (0.5–2.7)	<0.8 (<0.8–2.0)	<0.5 (<0.5–<0.5)	—	—	6.4
Calcium	mg	193 (160–228)	191 (159–204)	145 (131–182)	173 (140–204)	188 (162–234)	128 (107–148)	—	360	—
Chlorine	mg	207 (172–264)	275 (213–338)	204 (145–308)	210 (163–290)	321 (212–432)	163 (137–214)	—	275–700	—
Chromium	µg	0.74 (0.34–1.2)	0.52 (0.42–1.4)	2.8 (2.2–5.3)	2.2 (1.1–3.1)	1.2 (0.6–3.2)	0.50 (0.26–1.3)	—	10–40	—
Cobalt	µg	0.15 (0.09–0.46)	0.10 (0.05–0.17)	0.41 (0.22–0.65)	0.89 (0.48–1.67)	0.22 (0.10–0.38)	0.17 (0.07–0.32)	—	—	—
Copper	µg	167 (124–225)	136 (100–193)	178 (139–231)	198 (139–278)	149 (82–242)	94 (59–154)	480	500–700	3000
Fluorine	µg	6.0 (4.5–9.5)	9.2 (6.5–13.2)	16 (6–32)	75 (33–104)	14 (8–17)	3.2 (?–35)	—	100–500	—
Iodine	µg	38 (17–74)	43 (17–66)	40 (10–73)	36 (16–57)	45 (22–110)	7.0 (2.8–54)	—	40	—
Iron	µg	220 (118–325)	245 (178–375)	336 (207–528)	460 (258–737)	357 (242–524)	260 (146–601)	—	10000	4800
Lead	µg	1.8 (<0.6–4.3)	10 (7–17)	3.1 (1.5–6.0)	11 (6–15)	13 (11–19)	2.3 (<0.5–5.2)	—	—	21
Magnesium	mg	22 (17–26)	22 (17–26)	19 (12–22)	19 (16–22)	27 (23–37)	18 (15–21)	40	50	—
Manganese	µg	2.4 (1.6–4.3)	2.7 (1.4–5.5)	10 (6–21)	25 (13–42)	2.6 (1.9–3.8)	5.2 (1.6–14)	—	500–700	—

Element	Unit									
Mercury	µg	1.0 (0.5–2.0)	1.0 (0.5–1.9)	1.4 (0.8–3.2)	1.1 (0.6–2.9)	2.7 (1.5–4.0)	1.2 (1.9–9.1)	—	—	4 [g]
Molybdenum	µg	1.3 (0.2–3.2)	<0.3 (<0.3–2.3)	1.7 (0.7–4.5)	10 (5–18)	0.3 (<0.3–1.9)	0.6 (<0.2–1.8)	12	30–60	—
Nickel	µg	8.2 (3.0–14.5)	9.6 (5.9–14.9)	7.8 (3.0–13.7)	10.3 (6.6–16.9)	8.8 (5.8–14.0)	2.3 (<0.9–12.4)	—	—	—
Phosphorus	mg	98 (89–112)	91 (80–105)	94 (82–114)	94 (86–212)	114 (105–120)	72 (57–86)	—	240	—
Potassium	mg	310 (256–354)	371 (338–423)	263 (209–360)	300 (255–349)	438 (379–495)	239 (206–276)	—	350–925	—
Selenium	µg	12 (7–18)	9.3 (7.8–11.4)	16 (11–23)	21 (15–28)	10.5 (7.7–15)	9.0 (6.0–13)	—	10–40	—
Sodium	mg	67 (49–90)	70 (59–107)	56 (34–86)	82 (60–119)	70 (53–144)	56 (43–85)	—	115–350	—
Tin	µg	1.5 (1.4–6.5)	—	—	—	—	0.6 (0.3–0.8)	—	—	12000
Vanadium	µg	0.13 (0.09–0.31)	0.07 (0.05–0.15)	0.30 (0.19–0.44)	0.44 (0.26–0.61)	0.10 (0.05–0.12)	0.13 (0.05–0.70)	—	—	—
Zinc	mg	1.7 (0.7–3.9)	0.8 (0.4–1.3)	1.1 (0.7–1.8)	1.3 (0.8–1.8)	0.6 (0.3–0.8)	0.9 (0.5–1.3)	3.1 [f]	3	6

[a] Daily intake calculated as median concentration times median volume of milk consumed. Range gives 16th to 84th percentile (see text).
[b] These recommended daily allowances are based primarily on the amount provided by human milk, but in some cases they provide for infants receiving formula and other infant feeds.
[c] For a body weight of 6 kg (7).
[d] Recommended dietary allowance or estimated safe and adequate daily intakes for infants of 0–6 months of age (36).
[e] For a body weight of 6 kg.
[f] Assuming a bioavailability of 40%.
[g] Provisional tolerable weekly intake for adults set at 0.3 mg (0.005 mg/kg of body weight) (38).

Philippines). There are no recommendations from NAS or WHO with which to compare these figures.

Arsenic

The relatively high daily intake figure of 12 μg (range 5–20 μg) for Filipino babies in relation to about 1μg or less in the other five countries may perhaps be a cause for concern (though biological forms of arsenic are thought to be excreted relatively efficiently in the urine). Arsenic levels in tissues and body fluids directly reflect differences in dietary intake of this element. For example, high values have been observed in blood (China (Province of Taiwan) and Japan), breast milk (the Philippines), and liver and hair (India and Japan) (*42*), probably reflecting geochemically high levels of arsenic in these parts of Asia.

Cadmium

With the exception of Nigeria, the median intake values reported in Table 32 are all considerably below the provisional tolerable intakes proposed by a joint FAO/WHO Expert Committee (*37*). From the figures presented in Table 7, it would appear that approximately 20% of the intake values in Nigeria and more than 10% of the values in Guatemala are in excess of the provisional tolerable intake. Whether these findings are correct, or possibly caused by contamination of the milk specimens prior to analysis, is not known, but in any case further investigation in these countries would appear to be advisable. Iron deficiency, which is common in many developing countries, is believed to enhance cadmium absorption in humans by as much as fourfold (*44*), and might be considered as a possible cause of the elevated cadmium concentrations in the milk specimens. However, at least in Nigeria, this does not appear to be the case, since iron levels in the Nigerian milk samples were normal.

Calcium

As would be expected for an element that is under homoeostatic control, daily intakes of calcium through mother's milk all fall within a relatively narrow range. Most of the median values found in this study (Table 32) are only around 50% of the NAS recommended intake, or less, indicating that the latter may include an overgenerous margin of safety. It may be interesting in this regard to note that a Joint FAO/WHO Expert Group (*43*) assumed that the adequately breast-fed infant received sufficient calcium for its needs, and that the NAS report itself (*36*) states that the calcium needs of the infant are fully met by breast-feeding.

Chlorine

The intake values reported in Table 32 mostly fall within a relatively narrow range. They are generally below the estimated safe and adequate intake figures proposed by NAS, indicating that the latter may have been set too high.

Chromium

The median intake values for chromium reported in Table 32 vary from 0.5 µg per day in Zaire to 2.8 µg per day in Nigeria, and are all considerably below the estimated safe and adequate intake range proposed by NAS. These discrepancies are perhaps not surprising in view of the analytical difficulties associated with this element (8, 19), and a reassessment of the recommended intakes, on the basis of reliable analytical data, would now appear to be necessary. As mentioned previously, the analytical results obtained in this study may, if anything, be overestimates of the real values, indicating possibly an even greater discrepancy with the present NAS recommendations.

Cobalt

The intake values for cobalt found in this study vary significantly between study areas. However, by virtue of the fact that this element is needed only in the form of vitamin B_{12}, an assessment of total cobalt levels in human milk has only limited value in relation to nutrition. The recommended daily dietary allowance for infants of 0.1 µg of vitamin B_{12} corresponds to about 0.004 µg of cobalt per day, a value that is exceeded in all study areas.

Copper

Median intakes of copper in this study varied between 94 µg per day (Zaire) and 198 µg per day (the Philippines), and were all lower than the 480 µg per day recommended by WHO or the 500–700 µg per day estimated by NAS as the safe and adequate intake range.

Fluorine

Median intakes of fluorine in this study (Table 32) varied between 3.2 µg per day (Zaire) and 75 µg per day (the Philippines). With the exception of the Philippines, all values are smaller by an order of magnitude or more than the estimated safe and adequate intake range of 100–500 µg per day recommended by NAS. However, even for breast-fed infants, drinking water may be assumed to be an additional source of fluorine, and this may raise total intake to the recommended levels in many areas of the world.

Iodine

Median intakes of iodine in this study (Table 32), with one exception (Zaire), were within the narrow range of 36–45 μg per day, in remarkable agreement with the dietary allowance of 40 μg per day recommended by NAS. The low median intake of 7 μg per day in Zaire is consistent with the fact that iodine deficiency is highly prevalent in Kivu province, where the study was conducted.

Iron

Median intakes of iron in this study (Table 32) varied between 220 μg per day (Guatemala) and 460 μg per day (Philippines), and all were much lower than the 10 000 μg per day recommended by NAS. The NAS recommendation, however, assumes a bioavailability of 10% of the iron consumed, which may be close to reality for breast-milk substitutes but not for breast milk. It should also be noted that the FAO/WHO maximum tolerable daily intake, when calculated on the basis of a body weight of 6 kg, is less than the dietary daily allowance recommended by NAS. These recommendations thus appear inconsistent with each other.

Lead

Median intakes of lead in this study (Table 32) varied widely between 1.8 μg per day (Guatemala) and 13 μg per day (Sweden). However, even the higher values observed in Sweden are much less than the provisional tolerable weekly intake proposed in the 30th report of the Joint FAO/WHO Expert Committee on Food Additives (41).

Magnesium

As would be expected for an element that is under homoeostatic control, daily intakes of magnesium through mother's milk all fall within a relatively narrow range. The median values found in this study (Table 32) were in the range 18–27 mg per day, about half of the intake recommended by NAS and WHO, indicating that these recommendations may include an over-generous margin of safety.

Manganese

Median intakes of manganese in this study (Table 32) varied considerably between 2.4 μg per day (Guatemala) and 25 μg per day (the Philippines), all of which are more than an order of magnitude lower than the estimated safe and adequate intake range of 500–700 µg per day proposed by NAS. Obviously, some reassessment of the latter estimate is called for.

Mercury

All the median values found in this study (Table 32) are lower than the provisional tolerable intake of 4 µg per day proposed by an FAO/WHO Expert Committee (38). However, as the figures presented in Table 19 show, in all six countries, some samples were in excess of the proposed limit, e.g., in Nigeria slightly more than 10% of the samples and in Zaire slightly more than 25% of the samples. Whether these findings are accurate, or possibly caused by analytical problems or contamination of the milk specimens prior to analysis, is not known, but in any case further investigation in these countries would appear to be advisable. The country with the highest median intake was Sweden with 2.7 µg per day. It is possible that this increased mercury content of human milk may be related to the fact that much fish is consumed in the country, but this requires further investigation.

Molybdenum

Median intakes of molybdenum in this study (Table 32) varied widely between less than 0.3 µg per day (Hungary) and 10 µg per day (the Philippines). With the exception of the data for the Philippines, the values were all one or more orders of magnitude lower than the estimated safe and adequate intake range of 30–60 µg per day proposed by NAS and the daily intake of 12 µg per day recommended by WHO, indicating that these recommendations may be in need of revision.

Nickel

Median intakes of nickel in this study (Table 32) were mostly in the rather narrow range of 8–10 µg per day with the exception of Zaire where the median intake was only 2.3 µg per day. There are no recommended intakes from NAS or WHO with which to compare these figures.

Phosphorus

As with calcium, the intakes of phosphorus observed in this study (Table 32) all fell within a relatively narrow range (72–114 mg per day) and were all less than half of the dietary allowance (240 mg per day) recommended by NAS. However, the ratios of calcium to phosphorus were all within the desirable range of 1.5 to about 2.0 discussed in the NAS report (36).

Potassium

The intake values reported in Table 32 fall within a relatively narrow range of 239–438 mg per day. Some of them are somewhat below the safe and adequate intake range proposed by NAS, indicating that the latter is probably slightly too high.

Selenium

Median intakes of selenium observed in this study (Table 32) varied significantly between 9 µg per day (Zaire) and 21 µg per day (the Philippines). These are at the lower end of the estimated safe and adequate intake range suggested by NAS.

Sodium

As would be expected for an element that is under homoeostatic control, the daily intakes of sodium through mother's milk observed in this study (Table 32) all fell within a relatively narrow range. All of the median values reported (56–82 mg per day) were considerably lower than the estimated safe and adequate intake range of 115–350 mg per day proposed by NAS, indicating that this may include an over-generous margin of safety.

Tin

Results for tin in human milk are available from only two of the countries included in this study (Table 32). Median intakes were respectively 0.6 µg per day (Zaire) and 1.5 µg per day (Guatemala), both of which are several orders of magnitude lower than the maximum tolerable daily intake (*39*). The danger of excessive ingestion of tin by breast-fed infants is practically nil since the absorption of this element from the gastrointestinal tract is very low; therefore, mothers who are exposed to high intakes of this element for any reason are unlikely to secrete a significant amount into their milk.

Vanadium

Median intakes of vanadium observed in this study (Table 32) varied widely from 0.07 µg per day (Hungary) to 0.44 µg per day (the Philippines). There are no recommendations from WHO or NAS with which to compare these figures.

Zinc

Median intakes of zinc observed in this study (Table 32) varied by a factor of three between 0.6 mg per day (Sweden) and 1.7 mg per day

(Guatemala). All these values are considerably lower than the dietary allowance recommended by NAS or WHO, and the provisional tolerable daily intake recommended by a Joint FAO/WHO Expert Committee (*39*).

The fact that many of the intake values for essential trace elements discussed in this chapter are lower than the values recommended previously by WHO and NAS is open to three interpretations: (1) there may be differences in the dietary supply; (2) there may be uncertainties concerning the recommended intakes; or (3) there may be errors arising from analytical pitfalls owing to lack of adequate quality control or inadequate methodologies in the study.

Differences in the dietary supply of minor and trace elements are already well documented in a wide variety of different population groups, particularly for the elements iodine, fluorine, selenium and zinc. As for recommended dietary allowances, more accurate information is progressively becoming available. Reconsideration of recommendations based on data that were available 15–20 years ago is therefore justified. Regarding analytical shortcomings, the present state of analysis for trace elements in biological materials is still poor for many of the elements of interest, and major efforts are needed to improve the situation. It is for this reason that analytical quality assurance has received such attention in this project.

5. Conclusions

It can be concluded from this study that when minor and trace elements are determined under similar conditions in the breast milk of groups of mothers living in different parts of the world, environmental conditions appear to play a major role in determining the concentrations of most of them. However, for some of the elements (calcium, chlorine, magnesium, phosphorus, potassium and sodium), there appears to be little difference between groups and countries. The differences between median concentrations for these elements are less than 20% between countries and may even be as low as 7% as in the case of phosphorus. Concentrations of these elements in breast milk are probably controlled by homoeostatic mechanisms, which account for the small variations.

There is a second category of elements where differences between study areas may be very large, although similar values may be found in a majority of countries. This is the case for instance of iodine; in five countries participating in the study, iodine concentrations in breast milk varied very narrowly and it was in one study area only that a low figure was found. Such variations in concentrations probably reflect variations in environmental conditions or food habits. The nutritional status of the mother, as reflected by her socioeconomic status, does not appear to influence significantly the concentrations of minor and trace elements in breast milk. The ranges of concentrations found under usual conditions, i.e., after excluding study areas where exceptionally low or high values were observed, are given in Table 33. These ranges may be useful in determining the desirable concentration of trace elements in breast-milk substitutes; this, however, does not apply to toxic elements such as cadmium, lead and mercury. It may be opportune in this context to reconsider the recommendation of a WHO Expert Committee in 1973 (7) that milk formula products for babies should contain all the minor and essential trace elements at least in those levels that are present in human milk. The emphasis then was on the need to meet minimum nutritional requirements. Nowadays, one might also wish to express concern over the possibility that such formulations may contain excessive levels of some trace elements, to an extent far exceeding the normal nutritional requirements of babies during the first few months of life.

Table 33.   Range of trace element concentrations in breast milk observed under usual ("normal") conditions

Element	Range	
Antimony	1–4	µg/l
Arsenic	0.2–0.6	µg/l
Cadmium	<1	µg/l
Calcium	220–300	mg/l
Chlorine	320–410	mg/l
Cobalt	0.15–0.35	µg/l
Chromium	0.8–1.5	µg/l
Copper	180–310	µg/l
Fluorine	7–17	µg/l
Iodine	55–65	µg/l
Iron	350–720	µg/l
Lead	2–5	µg/l
Magnesium	29–38	mg/l
Manganese	3–4	µg/l
Mercury	1.4–1.7	µg/l
Molybdenum	0.3–3.0	µg/l
Nickel	11–16	µg/l
Phosphorus	135–155	mg/l
Potassium	410–550	mg/l
Selenium	13–24	µg/l
Sodium	90–130	mg/l
Tin	~1	µg/l
Vanadium	0.1–0.3	µg/l
Zinc	0.7–2.0	mg/l

References

1. *Contemporary patterns of breast-feeding. Report on the WHO Collaborative Study on Breast-feeding.* Geneva, World Health Organization, 1981.
2. *The quantity and quality of breast milk. Report on the WHO Collaborative Study on Breast-feeding.* Geneva, World Health Organization, 1985.
3. UNDERWOOD, E. J. *Trace elements in human and animal nutrition.* 4th ed. New York, Academic Press, 1977.
4. HURLEY, L. S. *Developmental nutrition.* Prentice-Hall, 1979, p. 188.
5. PRASAD, A. S. *Clinical and biochemical significance of zinc.* New York, Alan Liss, 1982.
6. YANG, G. Q. Keshan disease: an endemic selenium-related deficiency disease. In: Chandra, R. K., ed., *Trace elements in nutrition of children*, New York, Raven Press, 1985.
7. WHO Technical Report Series, No. 532, 1973 (*Trace elements in human nutrition: report of a WHO Expert Committee*).
8. PARR, R. M. Quality assurance of trace element analysis, health effects and interactions of essential and toxic elements (Proceedings of a Symposium held in Sweden, June 1983), *Nutrition research*, special supplement I, 5–11 (1985).
9. *Information sheet for reference material A-11, milk powder.* International Atomic Energy Agency, Vienna, 1980 (unpublished document).
10. MURAMATSU, Y. & PARR, R. M. *Survey of currently available reference materials for use in connection with the determination of trace elements in biological and environmental materials.* Vienna, International Atomic Energy Agency, 1985 (unpublished document IAEA/RL/128).
11. IYENGAR, G. V. & PARR, R. M. Quality assurance procedures developed for an international project on minor and trace elements in human milk, production, regulation and analysis of infant formula (*Proceedings of a conference*), Association of Official Analytical Chemists, Arlington, VA, 1985, 233–245.
12. McGILL, R. ET AL. Variations of box plots. *The American statistician*, **32**: 12–16 (1978).
13. IYENGAR, G. V. *Elemental composition of human and animal milk.* Vienna, International Atomic Energy Agency, 1982 (unpublished document IAEA-TECDOC-269).
14. BYRNE, A. R. ET AL. Results of a co-ordinated research programme to improve the certification of IAEA milk powder A-11 and animal muscle H-4 for eleven "difficult" trace elements. *Fresenius Zeitung zur analytische Chemie*, **326**: 723–729 (1987).
15. DANG, H. S. ET AL. Breast feeding: Mo, As, Mn, Zn and Cu concentrations in milk of economically poor Indian tribal and urban women. *Science of the total environment*, **44**: 177–182 (1985).
16. KOSTA, L. ET AL. Trace elements in some human milk samples by radiochemical neutron activation analysis. *Science of the total environment*, **29**: 261–268 (1983).
17. CORTES-TORO, E. *A study of trace elements in mother's milk and food for suckling infants: final report to the IAEA on research contract No. 2738.* Vienna, International Atomic Energy Agency, 1984 (unpublished document).
18. DANG, H. S. ET AL. Daily requirements of Fe, Co and Se during infancy. *Journal of radioanalytical and nuclear chemistry*, **84**: 177–183 (1984).

19. PARR, R. M. Problems of chromium analysis in biological materials: An international perspective with special reference to results for analytical quality control samples. *Journal of radioanalytical chemistry*, **39**: 421–433 (1977).
20. KUMPULAINEN, J. ET AL. Determination of chromium in human milk, serum and urine by electrothermal atomic absorption spectrophotometry without preliminary ashing. *Science of the total environment*, **31**: 71–80 (1983).
21. CASEY, C. E. & HAMBIDGE, K. M. Chromium in human milk from American mothers. *British journal of nutrition*, **52**: 73 (1984).
22. BELAVADY B. Lipid and trace element composition of human milk. *Acta paediatrica Scandinavica*, **67**: 566 (1978).
23. ESALA, S. ET AL. Effect of maternal fluorine intake on breast milk fluorine content. *British journal of nutrition*, **48**: 201–204 (1982).
24. BACKER, D. O. ET AL. Total and free ionic fluoride in human and cow's milk as determined by gas liquid chromatography and the fluoride electrode. *Caries research*, **8**: 181–186 (1974).
25. KERMARKAR, M. G. & RAMAKRISHNAN, C. V. Studies on lactation. Relation between the dietary intake of lactating women and the chemical composition of milk with regard to principle and certain inorganic constituents. *Acta paediatrica*, **49**: 599–604 (1960).
26. MURRAY, M. J. ET AL. The effect of iron status of Nigerian mothers on that of their infants at birth and 6 months, and on the concentration of Fe in breast milk. *British journal of nutrition*, **39**: 627–630 (1978).
27. ALTMAN, P. L. & DITTMER, D. S., ed. *Biology data book*. Bethesda, MD, Federal American Society of Experimental Biology, 1974.
28. *Composition of mature human milk*. London, HM Stationery Office, 1977 (Report on Health and Social Security, No. 12).
29. MURAMATSU, Y. ET AL. Stable iodine contents in human milk related to dietary algae consumption. *Hoken butsuri*, **18**: 113–117 (1983).
30. VUORI, E. *Copper, iron, manganese and zinc in breast milk*. PhD. thesis (unpublished), University of Helsinki, Finland, 1979.
31. VAUGHAN, L. A. ET AL. Longitudinal changes in the mineral content of human milk. *American journal of clinical nutrition*, **32**: 2301–2306 (1979).
32. PICCIANO, M. F. Mineral content of human milk during a single nursing. *Nutrition report international*, **18**: 5 (1978).
33. SILLANPAA, M. *Micronutrients and the nutrient status of soils: A global study*. Rome, Food and Agriculture Organization of the United Nations, 1982 (FAO Soils Bulletin, No, 48).
34. GALSTER, W. A. Mercury in Alaskan Eskimo mothers and infants. *Environmental health perspectives*, **15**: 135–141 (1976).
35. GHELBERG, N. W. ET AL. The lead content of milk in an area with non-ferrous metallurgical industry. *Igiena (Bucharest)*, **21**: 17–22 (1972).
36. *Recommended dietary allowances*, 9th rev. ed. Washington, DC, National Academy of Sciences 1980.
37. WHO Technical Report Series, No. 505, 1972 *and* FAO Nutrition Meetings Report Series, No. 51, 1972 (*Evaluation of certain food additives and the contaminants: mercury, lead and cadmium*: sixteenth report of the Joint FAO/WHO Expert Committee on Food Additives).
38. WHO Technical Report Series, No. 631, 1978 (*Evaluation of certain food additives and contaminants*: twenty-second report of the Joint FAO/WHO Expert Committee on Food Additives).
39. WHO Technical Report Series, No. 683, 1982 (*Evaluation of certain food additives and contaminants*: twenty-sixth report of the Joint FAO/WHO Expert Committee on Food Additives).
40. WHO Technical Report Series, No. 696, 1983 (*Evaluation of certain food additives and contaminants*: twenty-seventh report of the Joint FAO/WHO Expert Committee on Food Additives).
41. WHO Technical Report Series, No. 751, 1987 (*Evaluation of certain food additives*

and contaminants: thirtieth report of the Joint FAO/WHO Expert Committee on Food Additives).

42. IYENGAR, G. V. *Concentrations of fifteen trace elements in some selected adult human tissues and body fluids of clinical interest from several countries: results of a pilot study for the establishment of reference values.* Jülich, Kernforschungsanlage, 1985(unpublished document, Jülich Report No. 1974).

43. WHO Technical Report Series, No. 230, 1962 (*Calcium requirements*: report of an FAO/WHO Expert Group).

44. FLANAGAN, P. R. ET AL. Increased dietary cadmium absorption in mice and human subjects with iron deficiency. *Gastroenterology*, **74**: 841–846 (1978).

Collection of breast-milk samples for analysis

Samples of milk were collected by completely emptying one breast at a fixed time of day and at a fixed interval after the previous feed. Samples were usually collected by breast-pump at around 12 noon at the end of a four-hour period during which there had been no breast-feeding.

IAEA provided special Pyrex glass vessels (see Annex 1, Fig. 1) for the collection of samples in which trace elements were to be determined. Since even the slightest contamination would have disturbed the analysis, special precautions were taken to clean the vessels thoroughly before use with strong acid (see page 125).

Method of collection

The general principle was to extract milk from one breast until it was empty; the baby was then fed from the other breast. The whole sample was transported back to the local laboratory where it was homogenized and divided into several aliquots. The steps followed are given below.

(1) A carefully cleaned collection vessel of the appropriate design was used for the collection.

(2) The nipple and the area surrounding it were cleaned with detergent and water, rinsed with distilled water, and then patted dry with clean paper tissues.

(3) Milk was extracted from one breast until there was no, or almost no, further secretion. This took 5–10 minutes. The baby was then fed from the other breast.

(4) For transport back to the local laboratory, the sample was transferred to a pre-cleaned polyethylene vial.

(5) The vial was marked indelibly with an appropriate code number using a felt-tipped pen.

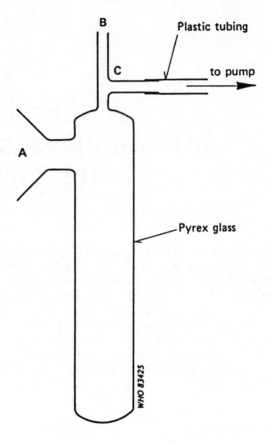

Annex 1, Fig. 1. Collection vessel

(6) The vial was then cooled by immersing it in ice-cold water, and was transferred in a refrigerated state to the local laboratory where the sample was homogenized.

(7) An aliquot of approximately 20–30 ml was transferred to another polyethylene vial and placed immediately in a deep-freeze unit (at −15°C) and stored in this way until it could be shipped to IAEA, Vienna, Austria.

Some special considerations regarding the collection procedure

(a) Use of detergent

A detergent (baby shampoo) was provided by IAEA for washing the breasts prior to sample collection. The concentrated detergent was diluted before use by adding one volume of the detergent to 25 volumes of distilled water. This was done in a clean glass vessel (beaker or bottle).

The nipple and the area surrounding it were washed with this solution, rinsed thoroughly with distilled water, and then patted dry with clean paper tissues.

(b) Use of the milk collection vessels

These vessels are designed to be used with a mechanical suction pump of some kind, either hand-operated (preferably made of plastic) or powered by electricity. The instructions given below were prepared for the collection of the milk sample:

(i) Connect the vacuum tubing from the pump to the collection vessel at outlet C (see Annex 1, Fig. 1), using the plastic tubing provided. Note that this tubing is required in order that outlet C remains clean and uncontaminated.

(ii) Apply opening A to the breast and turn on the pump.

(iii) Control the degree of suction by means of a finger applied to outlet B. The mother should preferably do this herself with a washed finger. If the pump is of a type that provides intermittent suction of the right kind, opening B should be kept closed either with a finger as suggested above or with the polyethylene cap provided.

(iv) When the collection of milk is complete, disconnect the plastic tubing from outlet C (in case of difficulty a small longitudinal cut may be made in the tubing with a razor blade). Then tip the vessel slowly and carefully so as to transfer the whole of the contents to a pre-cleaned polyethylene vial through outlet C.

(c) Cleaning of the milk collection vessels prior to re-use

The vessels provided by IAEA had been carefully cleaned and could be used once without further preparation (except possibly sterilization if this was considered desirable).

Before subsequent re-use, the collection vessels, plastic tubing, and polyethylene caps were washed in warm soapy water and rinsed. The glass collection vessels were then soaked in a 1:1 mixture of concentrated sulfuric acid and nitric acid for at least 30 minutes. The plastic tubing and polyethylene caps were soaked in dilute nitric acid (one part of concentrated nitric acid added to 10 parts distilled water) for at least 30 minutes. Everything was rinsed several times with distilled water, followed by a final rinse with quartz-distilled water (or demineralized distilled water) and shaken dry. The glass collection vessels (but not the other components) were wrapped lightly in aluminium foil and sterilized by heating for at least one hour in an oven at approximately 110°C.

Coding of the sample

The following system of coding was used. It consisted of six items separated by obliques:

Item 1—code number of the study area (2 digits);

Item 2—code number of the study group (1.urban elite, 2.urban poor, 3.traditional rural) (1 digit);

Item 3—serial number of the mother (4 digits);

Item 4—duration of breast-feeding (months) at time of collection (2 digits);

Item 5—year of collection (2 digits);

Item 6—calendar month of collection (2 digits).

Shipment of samples to the analytical centre

Minor and trace elements were analysed by IAEA or, under its supervision, in a designated laboratory. When a suitable number of samples had been collected, they were shipped to IAEA in Vienna in low-temperature transport containers, which kept them frozen at $-11\,°C$.

Preparation for analysis

Prior to analysis, the milk samples were reconstituted in liquid form by thawing; the vial was then put in a sonicator (ultrasonic bath) for about 5 minutes.

For the analysis of some constituents, and when there was no other alternative, some pooling of samples may have been necessary. In such cases, care was taken to ensure that the samples so pooled had all been obtained from a homogeneous group of mothers (same area, same study group).

Modified report form adopted for reporting results of minor and trace element determinations

The form shown on page 128 was used for reporting data on all minor and trace element analyses. Each page was used for one constituent only, and the completed forms were submitted to IAEA.

Data were entered in the columns as follows:

Column	
3–4	Code number of the study area (see note (a), p. 129)
5	Code number of the study group (see note (b), p. 129)
6–9	Serial number of the mother
10–11	43 is precoded: card serial number
12–13	Code number of the analytical laboratory (see note (c), p. 129)
14–15	Duration of feeding in months, at time of collection (age of child)
16–17	Year of collection
18–19	Calendar month of collection
20–22	Dry matter expressed as grams per litre of original milk
23–25	Constituent analysed: abbreviated name (see note (d), p. 129)
26–27	Constituent analysed; code number
28	Pooling "flag" (see *Instructions for pooled samples*, p. 129)
29–35	Concentration of the element (in grams or milligrams) per litre of liquid milk (expressed in scientific notation with a decimal exponent; e.g., 172.4 was written as $1.72E+2$; 0.3487 was written as $3.85E-1$; 2.75 was written as $2.75E00$). If a measurement was made with a result below the limit of detection, 0 (zero) was entered in this field.
36	Unit for concentration data ($1 = g/l$; $2 = mg/l$)

Report of analysis
Composition of human breast milk

Constituent:

Abbreviation

Code

Page

WHO 881036

Notes

(*a*) Columns 3–4: code number of the study area
    01 Guatemala
    03 Philippines
    04 Zaire
    05 Sweden
    06 Nigeria
    07 Hungary

(*b*) Column 5: code number of the study group (1 = urban elite; 2 = urban poor; 3 = traditional rural)

(*c*) Columns 12–13: code number of the analytical laboratory
    01 Guatemala
    03 Philippines
    04 Zaire
    05 Sweden
    06 Nigeria
    07 Hungary
    10 IAEA, Austria
    11 Federal Republic of Germany
    12 United Kingdom
    13 Yugoslavia
    14 Finland

(*d*) Columns 23–27: trace elements analysed
    Antimony (Sb), Arsenic (As), Cadmium (Cd), Calcium (Ca), Chlorine (Cl), Chromium (Cr), Cobalt (Co), Copper (Cu), Fluorine (F), Iodine (I), Iron (Fe), Lead (Pb), Magnesium (Mg), Manganese (Mn), Mercury (Hg), Molybdenum (Mo), Nickel (Ni), Phosphorus (P), Potassium (K), Selenium (Se), Sodium (Na), Tin (Sn), Vanadium (V), Zinc (Zn).

Instructions for pooled samples

The following instructions were issued regarding the pooling of samples.

(1) Whole specimens should, as far as possible, **not** be pooled. Only the aliquots required for the determination of individual constituents may be pooled, and then only if the analyst would otherwise be unable to carry out the analysis.

(2) The aliquots in a pool should:

    –all be from the same study group
    –all be for the same lactation period
    –all have been collected during the same trimester
    –all have the same volume.

(3) The pools so obtained should be distinguished from one another by a pool number (1, 2, 3, etc.). Numbering should start at 1 again for each different study group, lactation period, and trimester.

(4) Results for pooled samples should not be recorded under the serial code number (columns 6–9) for a mother. On the line with the mother's code number, write "1" in column 28[a] and leave the result field blank. Then record the result for the pooled sample on a separate line of the report form with the following data:

Column

6	Write "P" to indicate that these results are for pooled material
7	Pool number (1, 2, 3, etc., as specified in note (3) above)
8	Number of aliquots (different mothers) in the pool
9	Trimester number (1 = January–March; 2 = April–June; etc.)
16–19	(Year and month of collection) Leave blank.

---

[a] If the result is not available (if the sample was lost during analysis) write 2 in this column.

Analytical methods for the determination of calcium, chromium, magnesium, potassium and sodium

Reference laboratory

International Atomic Energy Agency, P.O. Box 100, A-1400 Vienna, Austria (contact person: Dr R. M. Parr; analyst: Ms E. Zeiller).

Analytical technique

Atomic absorption spectroscopy (AAS).

Method for calcium, magnesium, potassium and sodium

Description of method

Samples (usually 1 ml of liquid milk) were wet-ashed with HNO_3 and $HClO_4$ in closed Teflon containers for one hour at 105°C. The resulting solution was diluted with distilled water (usually by a factor of 100) and analysed directly by flame AAS (Perkin Elmer 460). An air/acetylene flame was used for magnesium, potassium and sodium and a N_2O/acetylene flame for calcium. A few of the earlier samples were analysed without preprocessing except for the precipitation of protein with trichloracetic acid. However, the method did not work well for sodium, owing to the high levels of this element in the filter paper used to remove the precipitated proteins, and was therefore abandoned.

Quality assurance

The results obtained for the two external quality control materials used in this programme, cow's milk powder A-11 and human milk HM-1, are shown in Annex 3, Table 1.

Annex 3, Table 1. Analysis for calcium, magnesium, potassium and sodium in the quality control materials: overall best estimate ± SD in mg/kg of dry matter (no. of measurements)

Element	A-11		HM-1
	This study	Certified value[a]	This study
Calcium	13 110 ± 10% (6)	12 900 ± 6.2%	2 290 ± 3.7% (5)
Magnesium	1 130 ± 5% (6)	1 100 ± 7.3%	257 ± 2.6% (6)
Potassium	17 600 ± 10% (6)	17 200 ± 5.8%	3 841 ± 3.5% (6)
Sodium	4 100 ± 10% (6)	4 420 ± 7.5%	822 ± 4.0% (6)

[a] Recommended concentration and 95% confidence interval.

For internal quality control purposes, to monitor the constancy of performance of the analytical methods throughout the whole analytical period, different samples of HM-1 were analysed at various times. The results shown in Annex 3, Table 2 record the values obtained expressed as a percentage of the respective overall mean concentration observed.

Although these results show some evidence of small fluctuations, they are insignificant in comparison with the biological variability in the specimens analysed. The analytical methods appear, therefore, to have worked with satisfactory accuracy and precision.

Method for chromium

Description of method

Samples of 25 μl of liquid milk were analysed directly by graphite furnace AAS (deuterium background correction, measurements at 357.6 nm). The method of standard additions was used (25-μl sample dried first, then 25 μl of standard or blank) with a heating cycle of

Annex 3, Table 2. Constancy of performance of the analytical methods for calcium, magnesium, potassium and sodium expressed as a percentage of the respective overall mean concentration observed

Stage	Calcium	Magnesium	Potassium	Sodium
beginning	104.2	100.3	101.3	97.0
	103.5	98.7	102.3	101.6
	96.5	99.1	102.4	100.7
	96.3	99.1	97.3	97.7
	—	97.8	94.0	96.0
end	99.4	105.0	102.7	106.8
overall	100.0 ± 3.7	100.0 ± 2.6	100.0 ± 3.6	100.0 ± 4.0

10 s at 100 °C, 20 s at 150 °C, 40 s at 1050 °C and 5 s at maximum temperature (2700 °C). Measurements were made with an integration time of 9 s using "gas stop".

Quality assurance

The results obtained for the two external quality control materials used in this programme, cow's milk powder A-11 and human milk HM-1, are shown in Annex 3, Table 3.

For internal quality control purposes, to monitor the constancy of performance of the analytical method throughout the whole analytical period, different samples of reconstituted A-11 milk powder were analysed with the results shown in Annex 3, Table 4.

The analytical method used for chromium was, for these samples, working very close to its limit of detection. The precision of the

Annex 3, Table 3.   Analysis for chromium in the quality control materials; overall best estimate ± SD in μg/kg of dry matter (no. of measurements)

A-11		HM-1	
This study	Expected	This study	Expected
18±30% (6)	18±21%[a]	9±60% (8)	8±5%[b]

[a] From: Byrne, A. R. et al. *Fresenius zeitung zur analytische Chemie*, **326**: 723–729 (1987).

[b] These values were reported by J. Kumpulainen (private communication) using a similar analytical method which had also been checked by analysis of a variety of reference materials including NBS bovine liver, SRM 1577 (Kumpulainen, J. et al., *Science of the total environment*, **31**: 71 (1983)).

Annex 3, Table 4.   Constancy of performance of the analytical method for chromium

Stage[a]	Value obtained	
	μg/l	% of overall mean
0	1.75±0.78	94±42
0	2.29±0.67	122±36
11	2.54±0.74	136±40
28	1.30±0.63	70±34
59	2.15±0.66	115±35
94	1.18±0.39	63±21

[a] Expressed in terms of number of "real" specimens analysed at that point of time, as a percentage of the total (0 = start of analysis, 100 = end)

analysis was, unfortunately, very poor. Nevertheless, as far as can be judged, the method appears to have been accurate.

Checks on the plastic vials in which the milk specimens were provided for analysis showed that they were not likely to have introduced any significant contamination.

Analytical methods for the determination of cadmium, chlorine and molybdenum

Reference laboratory

International Atomic Energy Agency, P.O. Box 100, A-1400 Vienna, Austria (Dr R. M. Parr).

Analytical technique

Neutron activation analysis (NAA).

Method for chlorine

Description of method

Samples of 50 mg of freeze-dried milk were analysed by instrumental NAA involving a five-minute activation at 10^{13} neutrons $\cdot$ cm$^{-2} \cdot$ s^{-1}. The samples were measured by gamma-ray spectrometry with a germanium detector starting about 10 minutes after the end of the activation. The measurement time was 5–10 minutes. Working standards were prepared from NH_4Cl.

Quality assurance

The results obtained for the two reference materials selected for use in the programme, cow's milk powder A-11 and human milk HM-1, are shown in Annex 4, Table 1. Two other reference materials, NBS bovine liver (SRM-1577) and Bowen's kale, were also analysed.

For internal quality control purposes, to monitor the constancy of performance of the analytical method throughout the whole analytical period, different samples of HM-1 were analysed at various times with the results shown in Annex 4, Table 2.

The results indicated that the analytical method was apparently working with satisfactory accuracy and precision.

Annex 4, Table 1. Analysis for chlorine in the quality control materials; overall best estimate $\pm$ SD in mg/kg of dry matter (no. of measurements)

Reference material	Concentration	
	This study	Certified value
NBS SRM 1577	2 549 ± 2.6% (6)	(2 700)[a]
Bowen's kale	3 567 ± 3.4% (6)	3 500 ± 8.6%[b]
A-11	9 920 ± 2.9% (8)	9 080 ± 19%[b]
HM-1	2 748 ± 3.9% (19)	

[a] Not certified (information value quoted in certificate of analysis).
[b] 95% confidence interval.

Annex 4, Table 2. Constancy of performance of the analytical method for chlorine in HM-1

State[a]	Value obtained	
	mg/kg	% of overall mean
5	2703	97.5
16	2836	102.3
27	2924	105.4
33	2733	98.6
43	2619	94.4
54	2776	100.1
66	2816	101.6
78	2605	93.9
89	2860	103.1
100	2859	103.1
overall	2773 ± 3.8%	100.0 ± 3.8

[a] Expressed in terms of the number of "real" specimens analysed at that point in time, as a percentage of the total (0 = start of analysis; 100 = end)

Method for cadmium and molybdenum

Description of method

Samples of 100 mg of freeze-dried milk were analysed by radiochemical NAA involving an irradiation for 48 hours at 7×10^{13} n.cm^{-2}.s^{-1}. After a decay time of about 4–5 days the samples were wet-ashed with H_2SO_4/H_2O_2 together with 10-μg carriers of each element. The two elements were then separated from other interfering elements on Dowex AG × 8 columns in the chloride form using a radiochemical separation scheme developed by Iyengar.[a] The Dowex columns were measured directly with a Ge gamma-ray spectrometer. Working standards were prepared from the oxides CdO and MoO_3 respectively.

Cadmium was determined from measurements of its daughter product indium-115 m (336.25 keV). In many of the human milk specimens (but not in the A-11 milk powder) the spectrometry was complicated by a background peak at 338.7 keV and by a contaminant peak at 340.47 keV (protactinium-233). In most of these samples the contaminant peaks could be resolved from the peak of interest by mathematical means, but in a few cases this was not possible; such measurements were recorded as having been unsuccessful.

Molybdenum was determined from measurements of its daughter product technetium-99m (140.51 keV). In many of the human milk specimens (but not in the A-11 milk powder) the spectrometry was complicated by contaminant peaks at 137.16 keV (rhenium-186) and 133.05 keV and other lines (hafnium-181). In most of these samples the contaminant peaks could be resolved from the peak of interest by mathematical means, but in a few cases this was not possible; such measurements were recorded as having been unsuccessful.

Quality assurance

Annex 4, Table 3 gives the results obtained for the two reference materials selected for use in this programme, cow's milk powder A-11 and human milk HM-1. Two other reference materials, NBS bovine liver (SRM 1577) and Bowen's kale, were also analysed.

For internal quality control purposes, to monitor the constancy of performance of the analytical method throughout the whole analytical period, different samples of NBS SRM 1577 were analysed at various times. The results are given in Annex 4, Table 4.

It is apparent from these data that, as far as can be judged, the analytical methods were accurate. However, for the milk samples, they were working close to their limits of detection. The latter varied somewhat from sample to sample depending on the interferences present, but were generally close to 0.01 mg/kg for cadmium and 0.003 mg/kg for molybdenum (both on a dry weight basis), or roughly ten times lower in mg/l.

Checks on the plastic vials in which the specimens were shipped from the collection centres showed that they were not likely to have introduced any significant contamination. The same applied to the

---

[a] Iyengar, G. V. *Procedural and developmental aspects of a multi-element automatic radiochemical machine applied to neutron irradiated biomedical samples*, Jülich Kernforschungsanlage, 1976 (Jülich Report No. 1308 (unpublished)).

Annex 4, Table 3. Analysis for cadmium and molybdenum in the quality control materials; overall best estimate $\pm$ SD in mg/kg of dry matter (no. of measurements)

Element	Reference material	Concentration	
		This study	Certified value[a]
Cadmium	NBS SRM 1577	0.31 ± 11% (6)	0.27 ± 15%
	Bowen's kale	0.92 ± 3.4% (6)	0.89 ± 10%
	A-11	< 0.006	(0.0017 ± 12%)[b]
	HM-1	< 0.006	
Molybdenum	NBS SRM 1577	3.35 ± 2.4% (6)	(3.4)[c]
	Bowen's kale	2.07 ± 7.8% (6)	2.3 ± 9.1%
	A-11	0.085 ± 11% (6)	(0.092 ± 10%)[b]
	HM-1	0.007 ± 50% (6)	—

[a] Limits show 95% confidence interval.
[b] New intercomparison data (Byrne, A. R. et al. Fresenius Zeitung zur analytische Chemie, **326**: 723–729 (1987)).
[c] Not certified (information value quoted in certificate of analysis).

Annex 4, Table 4. Constancy of performance of the analytical methods for cadmium and molybdenum

	Value obtained			
	Cadmium		Molybdenum	
Stage[a]	mg/kg	% of overall mean	mg/kg	% of overall mean
0	0.30	96	3.26	97.3
0	0.34	109	3.33	99.4
7	0.35	113	3.27	97.6
14	0.25	81	3.42	102.1
69	0.32	104	3.39	101.2
100	0.30	98	3.45	103.0
	0.31 ± 11%	100 ± 11	3.35 ± 2.4%	100 ± 2.4

[a] Expressed in terms of number of "real" specimens analysed at that point in time, as a percentage of the total (0 = start of analysis; 100 = end).

vials used for freeze-drying and storing the dried material prior to analysis, although it was discovered, in the middle of the study, that these vials contained relatively high concentrations of cadmium. Subsequent experiments showed, however, that significant contamination arose only when the liquid milk was in contact with the vials for a much longer time than was the case in practice.

Analytical methods for the determination of antimony, cobalt, copper, iron, manganese, mercury, selenium and zinc

Reference laboratory

Institut für Medizin, Kernforschungsanlage Jülich, PF 1913, D-5170 Jülich 1, Federal Republic of Germany (Dr G. V. Iyengar).

Analytical technique

Neutron activation analysis (NAA).

Method for copper and manganese

Description of method

The samples were analysed by radiochemical NAA. For each analysis about 100–150 mg of sample material was enclosed in a polyethylene vial. Irradiation was carried out for two minutes at about 10^{14} neutrons per cm² per second at 4 °C. After a decay period of one hour each sample was wet-ashed in 0.5 ml of concentrated H_2SO_4 with the aid of H_2O_2. The resulting solution was brought to pH 5–6 and passed through columns containing a chelating resin. The yield is quantitative for both copper and manganese.[a] The activities were measured with a germanium/lithium gamma-ray spectrometer.

---

[a] Iyengar, G. V. *Procedural and developmental aspects of a multi-element automatic radiochemical machine applied to neutron-irradiated biomedical samples.* Jülich, Kernforschungsanlage, 1976 (Jülich report, No. 1308 (unpublished)).

Quality assurance

Specimens of cow's milk powder A-11 and human milk HM-1 were included in each batch of human milk samples as shown in Annex 5, Table 1.

The results obtained are given in Annex 5, Tables 2 and 3. For A-11, comparison with the certified data for copper and manganese is complicated by the fact that the latter values are still the subject of some controversy.[a] Recent data suggest that the true values for copper and manganese in A-11 are probably close to 0.37 and 0.25 mg/kg respectively (see Annex 10, Table 1).[b] Comparison with the data reported in Annex 5, Table 3 shows that, on this basis, the analytical method would appear to have been working reliably.

Method for antimony, cobalt, iron, mercury, selenium and zinc

Description of method

The samples were analysed by instrumental NAA as described by Kasperek.[c] For each analysis about 100–200 mg of the sample material was sealed in a quartz tube and irradiated for two days at about 5×10^{13} neutrons cm^{-2} s^{-1}. An iron wire of about 4 mg in weight was also irradiated with each sample to monitor the neutron flux. After about 4–6 weeks of decay, the quartz tubes were opened under liquid nitrogen cooling, and the sample material was recovered, weighed and measured with the help of a 100 cm^3 Ge(Li) well-type detector connected to a 4096 channel pulse height analyser. Details of

Annex 5, Table 1.   Total number of samples analysed[a]

	Samples	HM-1	A-11
Guatemala	84	5	2
Hungary	71	8	3
Nigeria	18	1	2
Philippines	65	11	4
Sweden	32	4	3
Zaire	69	2	5
Total	339	31	19

$$^a \frac{\text{Reference samples}}{\text{Actual samples}} = 15\%$$

---

[a] de Goeij, J. J. M. et al. *Analytica chimica acta*, **146**: 161 (1983).
[b] Byrne, A. R. et al. *Fresenius Zeitung zur analytische Chemie*, **326**: 723–729 (1987).
[c] Kasperek, K. *Proceedings of the Second International Conference on Nuclear Methods in Environmental Research, Columbia, MO,* 1974.

Annex 5, Table 2.   Results for HM-1 aliquots analysed together with different groups of samples[a]

Sample groups (no. of aliquots)	Long irradiation					Short irradiation		
	Antimony (ng/g)	Cobalt (ng/g)	Iron (µg/g)	Mercury (ng/g)	Selenium (ng/g)	Zinc (µg/g)	Copper (µg/g)	Manganese (µg/g)
A. Guatemala (5)	14.2±5.5	1.0±0.2[b]	2.5±0.6	10.0±4.2	77.0±7.6	12.4±0.8	1.7±0.07	77.4±4.5
B. Philippines (11)	9.0±4.0	1.7±0.65	1.8±0.6	7.0±2.0	72.5±6.0	12.1±1.0	1.6±0.14	73.0±5.0
C. Zaire (2)[c,d]	14.5	4.9	4.88	115	90.5	9.6	1.75	81.5
	86	0.6	2.10	2	74	12.7	1.77	77.1
D. Sweden (4)	11.7±2.8	1.8±1.1	1.9±0.4	11.2±2.9	76.2±6.4	11.7±0.15	1.7±0.10	74.0±5.5
E. Nigeria (1)	5	0.84	1.6	8.2	70	11.2	1.8	84.1
F. Hungary (8)	10.2±4.6	1.4±0.64	1.8±0.4	6.0±2.9	92.3±16.2	14.3±0.9	1.5±0.06[e]	65.0±6.7[e]
G. A+B+D+E+F mean±SD (29)	11.0±4.6	1.5±0.7	1.95±0.57	7.75±3.4	79.1±12.8	12.7±1.34	1.6±0.14	72.3±7.1
	42%	47%	29%	43%	16%	11%	8.5%	9.8%
H. A+B+D+E, mean±SD (21)					74.1±6.4	12.5±0.9		
					8.7%	7.4%		
F/G					1.25	1.19		

[a] Two HM-1 aliquots analysed with samples from Guatemala showed higher values for cobalt, 9.7 and 10.6 ng/g, respectively. Both the HM-1 aliquots received along with samples from Zaire showed some inconsistencies; one showed high results for Co and Hg and a relatively low value for Zn (9.6 ng/g, average value for HM-1 = 12 ng/g). The other aliquot showed a high value for Sb.
[b] Two high values excluded (9.7, 10.6)
[c] Both aliquots from Zaire excluded from mean (see footnote a)
[d] Individual values
[e] Two low values (copper 1.2; manganese, 49) excluded from mean, because of sample loss while opening the tube.

Annex 5, Table 3. Results for A-11 aliquots analysed together with different groups of samples

Sample groups (no. of aliquots)	Long irradiation			Short irradiation	
	Cobalt (ng/g)	Iron (µg/g)	Zinc (µg/g)	Copper (µg/g)	Manganese (µg/g)
A. Guatemala (2)[a]	4.6[b]	3.0	32	0.41	240
	5.2	2.4	36	0.37	280
B. Philippines (4)	4.7±0.8	2.0±0.5	35.0±3.6	0.39±0.03	252±14
C. Zaire (5)	5.0±1.24	2.0±0.3	36.1±2.8	0.39±0.03	276±26
D. Sweden (3)	5.1±1.1	2.3±0.6	33.4±2.4	0.38±0.025	257±14
E. Nigeria (2)	5.3[b]	2.75	37	0.40	262
	4.2	1.9	32	0.42	306
F. Hungary (3)	5.9±1.72	2.52±0.53	40.0±4.8	0.38±0.03	249±27
G. Overall mean±SD	5.1±1.1 (21%)	2.24±0.48 (21%)	35.6±3.6 (10%)	0.389±0.024 (6%)	263±0.023 (9%)
H. A+B+C+D+E, mean±SD			34.7±2.84 (8%)		
F/H			1.15		

[a] Individual values.

the analytical steps are described elsewhere.[a] Since 100% recovery of the irradiated material is not possible without dissolving the sample along with the quartz, the sample recovered was weighed and this weight was used for evaluating the results. A long irradiation without cooling partially chars biological material and thereby causes a concentration of the residual matter.[b] It was observed that there was some degree of variation in the weights depending on the time between the opening of the quartz ampoule and the weighing of the sample. It was therefore necessary to record the weights at a standardized interval (within 24 hours of opening the quartz ampoules). The good agreement seen in the results for zinc in HM-1 (Table 2) and A-11 (Table 3) confirms that there was no serious fluctuation in the recorded weights. However, the Hungarian samples, which were the first to be analysed, were weighed over an interval sometimes extending to a few days after opening the ampoules. On the basis of the results obtained for zinc in HM-1 and A-11, the values obtained for the Hungarian milk specimens were probably too high by about 15–20%. A correction factor, reducing the values by 17.5%, was therefore applied to the data for Hungarian samples quoted elsewhere in this report.

Quality assurance

Specimens of cow's milk powder A-11 and human milk HM-1 were included in each batch of human milk specimens as shown in Annex 5, Table 1. The results obtained are given in Annex 5, Tables 2 and 3.

Annex 5, Table 4 presents a comparison, for cow's milk powder A-11, between the results of this study and the expected values.

Annex 5, Table 4. Comparison with expected values for milk powder A-11; overall best estimate ± SD in mg/kg of dry matter (no. of measurements)

	Concentration	
Element	This study	Certified value[a]
Cobalt	0.0051 ± 21% (19)	0.0045 ± 18%[b]
Iron	2.24 ± 21% (19)	3.65 ± 21%
Selenium	0.031 ± 13% (5)[b]	0.034 ± 21%
Zinc	34.7 ± 8% (16)	38.9 ± 5.9%

[a] Recommended concentration and 95% confidence interval.
[b] New intercomparison data (Byrne, A. R. et al. *Fresenius Zeitung zur analytische Chemie*, **326**: 723–729 (1987)).

[a] Iyengar, G. V. et al. *Physics in medicine and biology*, **23**: 66 (1978).
[b] Iyengar, G. V. et al. *Science of the total environment*, **24**: 267 (1982).

For cobalt, selenium and zinc, the agreement is satisfactory. For iron, the results obtained in this study are significantly lower than the so-called "certified value", which has, however, recently been called into question by Iyengar et al.[a] Further evidence in favour of the value given by Iyengar et al. is provided by Byrne et al.[b] who reported a value of 2.4 ± 0.06 (3) mg/kg[c] for iron in A-11.

For mercury and antimony, the analytical method used by the reference laboratory (instrumental NAA) was able to provide results for the HM-1 reference material (see Annex 5, Table 2) but unfortunately not for the A-11 reference material. This was because cow's milk contains a much higher amount of the interfering element phosphorus than does human milk. Thus, although there is no *a priori* reason for doubting the reliability of the analytical method for mercury and antimony, it has not yet been validated by means of any external quality control material.

In summary, the reliability of the analytical data appears to be reasonably well established for cobalt, iron, selenium and zinc, but is not yet proven for antimony and mercury.

Checks on the plastic vials in which the milk specimens were provided for analysis showed that they were not likely to have introduced any significant contamination for any of the elements under consideration.

---

[a] See footnote *b*, page 143.

[b] Byrne, A. R. et al. *Nuclear activation techniques in the life sciences. Proceedings of a symposium held in Vienna, 1978.* Vienna, International Atomic Energy Agency, 1979 (unpublished).

[c] Mean $\pm$ SD (no. of measurements).

Analytical methods for the determination of lead and nickel

Reference laboratory

Institute of Science and Technology, University of Manchester, P.O. Box 88, Manchester M60 1QD, England (Professor G. F. Kirkbright[a]).

Analytical techniques

Electrothermal atomization atomic absorption spectrometry (ETA-AAS) was used for lead and inductively coupled plasma optical emission spectrometry (ICP-OES) for nickel.

Methods

Description of methods

A weighed amount (usually 100 mg) of each specimen of freeze-dried milk powder was transferred to a mini Kjeldahl flask and wet-ashed with a mixture of H_2SO_4 and HNO_3. After adjusting the pH of the digest to 8.5–9.0, Ni(II) and Pb(II) were extracted into dithizone/chloroform. The extracts were then analysed for lead and nickel as quickly as was practical.

Lead was analysed by ETA-AAS using a model 305B atomic absorption spectrophotometer fitted with a deuterium arc background corrector and model HGA 2000 graphite furnace atomizer (Perkin-Elmer). The instrumental parameters used are summarized below.

Wavelength[b]	283.31 nm
Slits (bandpass)	0.3 nm

---

[a] Now deceased.

[b] Lead hollow cathode lamp operated at manufacturer's specifications, deuterium arc background correction employed.

Furnace programme

Argon flowrate	3 litres/min
Drying	100 °C, 30s
Ashing	400 °C, 30s
Atomization[a]	2000 °C, 4s
Sample volume	15 μl

Nickel was analysed by ICP-OES using a model HFP 2500 D spectrometer, with a 27.12 MHz plasma source and 2.5 kW generator matching unit and torch box (Plasma-Therm Inc., USA). The instrumental parameters used are summarized below.

Wavelength	352.45 nm
Slits	40 μm
Photomultiplier tube voltage	1.4 kV
Plasma gas flowrate	13.0 litres/min
Carrier gas flowrate	1.8 litres/min
Forward power	0.85 kW
Reflected power	2 W
Viewing height[b]	33 mm

Electrothermal vaporization programme

Drying	5.5V, 30s
Ashing	6.0V, 30s
Vaporization	9.0V, 3.5s
Sample volume	15 μl

Aqueous standards of both nickel and lead were used routinely as this method of calibration was faster and easier than standard additions and had been shown to yield satisfactory results. However, the method of standard additions was also utilized periodically over the time of the study in conjunction with direct standardization as a means of keeping a check on the method.

Quality assurance

The following results, overall best estimate ± relative SD (number of measurements) were obtained for one of the reference materials selected for use in this programme, human milk HM-1: lead, 0.09±32% (24) mg/kg of dry matter; nickel, 0.11±28% (24) mg/kg of dry matter.

For internal quality control purposes, to monitor the constancy of performance of the analytical method throughout the whole analytical

---

[a] 60-second cooling time allowed between end of atomization and injection of next sample.

[b] Measured from top of the load coil.

period, 24 different samples of HM-1 were analysed at various times. Some of the samples had been provided as "blind" specimens. The results obtained did not show any evidence of significant departures from the normal standards of performance of the analytical methods at any time during the study. However, since these methods were working close to their respective limits of detection for both lead and nickel, the constancy of performance could not be monitored very sensitively.

No data were reported for cow's milk, A-11, or any other certified reference materials, owing to the untimely death of Professor Kirkbright before completion of this project. For this reason, and because of the subsequent disbandment of his group, it was unfortunately not possible to follow up this matter any further.

Checks on the plastic vials in which the milk specimens were provided for analysis showed that they were not likely to have introduced any significant contamination.

In summary, although there are no *a priori* grounds for doubting the reliability of the data on nickel obtained in this study, it would clearly have been desirable to have done more work to validate the analytical methods used and to have improved their precision.

Analytical methods for the determination of arsenic, iodine, tin and vanadium

Reference laboratory

Jozef Stefan Institute, P.O. Box 522, YU-61001 Ljubljana, Yugoslavia (Dr A. R. Byrne).

Analytical technique

Neutron activation analysis (NAA) was used.

Method

Description of methods

All four elements were analysed by radiochemical NAA, using individual aliquots and specially devised radiochemical separation procedures for each element. This meant that, in general, because of the low levels of these elements present, an insufficient volume was available for concurrent analyses of all four elements in each milk sample. However, iodine analysis required only 50–100 mg of sample (or less, but this was judged to be a limit below which homogeneity problems might arise), so that it could normally be performed on a sample analysed for arsenic, which was the next least demanding in terms of sample size (200 mg or thereabouts). Hence results for vanadium, and the relatively few results for tin, are reported for subgroups of samples from each country and social group, which are distinct from those used for arsenic and iodine.

For the determination of arsenic, samples of 200–300 mg were irradiated in pre-cleaned polyethylene ampoules for 20–30 hours at a flux density of 2×10^{12} neutron $cm^{-2}s^{-1}$. Following wet-ashing with H_2SO_4 and HNO_3, and finally with H_2O_2, in the presence of arsenic carrier, the arsenic was extracted into toluene from an aqueous phase with the composition 3.6 mol/litre H_2SO_4 and 1.0 mol/litre KI. The activity was measured with a 7.6 cm × 7.6 cm (3 in × 3 in) well-type NaI(Tl) detector. Further details may be found elsewhere.[a]

For the determination of iodine, samples of 50–100 mg were irradiated in pre-cleaned polyethylene ampoules for 15–20 minutes at a flux density of 4×10^{12} neutrons $cm^{-2} s^{-1}$. A radiochemical separation was then applied which was based on ignition in a closed oxygen flask (4-litre capacity), followed by extraction of iodine into CCl_4, with a clean-up based on a selective redox extraction-stripping cycle, using HNO_2 and H_2SO_3. The activity was measured with a 7.6 cm × 7.6 cm (3 in × 3 in) well-type NaI(Tl) detector. Further details may be found elsewhere.[b]

For the determination of tin, samples of the maximum size possible, but at least 300 mg, were irradiated in pre-cleaned polyethylene ampoules for 10 min at a neutron flux density of 1×10^{14} neutrons $cm^{-2} s^{-1}$ in the DIDO reactor at Jülich, Federal Republic of Germany. A radiochemical separation was then applied based on wet-ashing with H_2SO_4 and HNO_3, and a clean-up by fuming with $HClO_4$, followed by extraction of tin tetraiodide into toluene, and selective washing of the organic phase to remove arsenic-76 and other contaminants. The activity was measured with a well-type Ge(Li) detector. Further details may be found elsewhere.[c]

For the determination of vanadium, samples of 200–300 mg were irradiated in pre-cleaned polyethylene ampoules for 2.25 min (the maximum allowable, due to heating effects) at a flux density of 5×10^{13} neutrons $cm^{-2} s^{-1}$ in the MERLIN reactor at Jülich. A radiochemical separation was then applied based on rapid wet-ashing (using the same method as for tin) followed by solvent extraction of vanadium with n-benzoylphenylhydroxylamine. The activity was measured with a well-type Ge(Li) detector. Because of the very short half-life of the vanadium-52 used for these measurements (3.75 min), all operations had to be carried out in as short a time as was practicable. Further details may be found elsewhere.[d]

[a] See: Byrne, A. R. *Analytica chimica acta,* **59**: 91 (1972), Byrne, A. R. & Vakselj, A. *Croatica chemica acta,* **46**: 225 (1974); and Dermelj, M. et al. *Talanta,* **23**: 856 (1976).

[b] Gourdjancic, I. et al. *Journal of radioanalytical chemistry,* **58**: 359 (1980).

[c] Byrne, A. R. & Gorenc, D. *Analytica chimica acta,* **59**: 81 (1972); and Byrne, A. R. *Journal of radioanalytical chemistry,* **20**: 627 (1974).

[d] Byrne, A. R. & Kosta, L., *Journal of radioanalytical chemistry,* **44**: 247 (1978); and Byrne, A. R. & Vrbic, V. *Journal of radioanalytical chemistry,* **54**: 77 (1979).

Annex 7, Table 1. Analysis of arsenic, iron, tin and vanadium in the quality control materials (overall best estimate $\pm$ SD in ng/kg of dry matter (no. of measurements)

Element	Reference material	Concentration (ng/g)	
		This study	Certified value[a]
Arsenic	A-11	4.8±0.2 (8)	4.85±4%[b]
	HM-1	1.3±0.3[c] (12)	—
	H-4	6.1±0.2 (6)	(~6)[b]
	SRM 1567	6.3±0.4 (6)	6[d]
	SRM 1568	464±11 (6)	410±50
Iodine	A-11	89.6±5.3 (4)	87±7%[b]
	HM-1	321±25 (21)	—
	H-4	22.4±1.9 (5)	(~14)[b]
	V-5	2.76±0.6 (6)	2.88±1.23
Tin	Bowen's kale	205±18 (2)	210±30
Vanadium	A-11	0.92±0.10 (7)	—
	HM-1	0.57±0.14 (16)	—
	H-4	3.0±0.2 (6)	(2.9±0.2(11))[e]

[a] Recommended concentration and 95% confidence interval
[b] Not certified (recent intercomparison data) Byrne, A. R. et al. *Fresenius Zeitung zur analytische Chemie*, **326**: 723–729 (1987).
[c] Plus 4 outliers between 3.0 and 20.3
[d] Not certified (information value quoted in certificate of analysis).
[e] Not certified (see reference 9)

Quality assurance

The results for the two reference materials selected for use in this programme, cow's milk powder A-11 and human milk HM-1, are shown in Annex 7, Table 1. Where available, results obtained for other reference materials are also quoted, i.e., for IAEA animal muscle H-4, IAEA wheat flour V-5, NBS wheat flour SRM 1567, and NBS rice flour SRM 1568.

Obviously, since certified reference materials for these elements were either not available, or were of inappropriate matrix composition, it was impossible to prove beyond all doubt that the analytical methods just described were working reliably in this study. Nevertheless, as far as can be judged from the results presented in Annex 7, Table 1, there are reasonable grounds for believing this to have been the case.

For internal quality control purposes, to monitor the constancy of performance of the analytical method throughout the whole analytical period, 24 different samples of HM-1 were analysed at various times. Some of the samples had been provided as "blind" specimens. The results obtained did not show any evidence of significant departures from the normal standards of performance of the analytical methods at any time during the study.

Checks on the plastic vials in which the milk specimens were provided for analysis showed that, for all four elements, they were not likely to have introduced any significant contamination.

Analytical method for the determination of fluorine

Reference laboratory

Department of Chemistry, Helsinki University of Technology, Otaniemi, SF-02150 Espoo 15, Finland (Professor L. Niinistö).

Analytical technique

Electrochemical analysis (ion-specific electrode) was used.

Method

Description of method

Samples of milk were weighed into pre-cleaned platinum crucibles, to which 1 ml of 0.2 mol/litre magnesium succinate solution was then added as a fixative. After freeze-drying followed by ashing in a muffle furnace, and dissolution in 40% perchloric acid containing 5% Ag_2O (to prevent the diffusion of chlorides), fluoride was separated by diffusion in a special cell on sodium hydroxide-treated Whatmann 114 filter paper for 24 hours at 60 °C. The excess portions of the filter paper were cut off, and the fluoride was eluted with 1 ml of deionized water and 2 ml of total ionic strength buffer (TISAB). A potentiometric determination of fluoride in the eluate was made using a Beckman 4500 mV-meter and Orion model 94-09 fluoride-selective electrode. Further details may be found elsewhere.[a]

Quality assurance

The results obtained for the two reference materials selected for use in this programme, cow's milk powder A-11 and human milk HM-1, are presented in Annex 8, Table 1.

---

[a] Esala, S. et al. *Mikrochimica acta (Vienna)*, **1**: 155 (1983).

Annex 8, Table 1. Analysis for fluorine in the quality control materials; overall best estimate $\pm$SD in mg/kg dry matter (no. of measurements)

Reference material	Concentration
A-11	0.176 $\pm$ 0.022 (24)
HM-1	0.054 $\pm$ 0.007 (14)

Unfortunately, there are still no certified data available for these, or any other biological reference materials, and it is, therefore, impossible to prove beyond all doubt that the analytical method was working reliably in this study. However, comparative data for Bowen's kale and NBS orchard leaves SRM-1571 reported by Esala et al.[a] lend support to this conclusion.

For internal quality control purposes, to monitor the constancy of performance of the analytical method throughout the whole analytical period, different samples of A-11 and HM-1 were analysed at various times. The results obtained are shown in Annex 8, Fig. 1. Although these data have a relative standard deviation of up to about 15%, there is no evidence of a significant trend with time, and in any case the analytical variability was generally much less than the biological variability in the samples analysed. As far as can be judged, therefore, the analytical method was working satisfactorily.

Checks on the plastic vials in which the milk specimens were provided for analysis showed that they were not likely to have introduced any significant contamination.

Annex 8, Fig. 1.   Analyses for fluorine (mg/g) in reference materials A-11 and HM-1

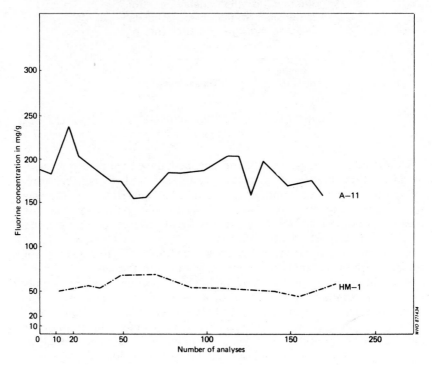

Analytical method for the determination of phosphorus

Reference laboratory

Forschungsinstitut für Kinderernährung, Heinstück 11, D-4600 Dortmund 50 (Brünninghausen), Federal Republic of Germany (Professor G. Schöch).

Analytical technique

Light absorption spectrometry (spectrophotometry) was used.

Method

Description of method

Individual samples of about 200 mg dry weight were ashed in a muffle furnace and the residues taken up in HCl. Phosphorus was determined spectrophotometrically as the molybdovanadate complex according to the method described by Estrin & Boland.[a] Most samples were analysed in duplicate.

Quality assurance

The results obtained for the two reference materials selected for use in this programme, cow's milk powder A-11 and human milk HM-1 are given in Annex 9, Table 1.

Although the agreement between the value reported for A-11 and the certified value is not perfect, this may be due to uncertainty in the quoted certified value. Phosphorus could not be recommended with a satisfactory degree of confidence in A-11.

---

[a] Estrin, B. & Boland, F. E. *Journal of the Association of Official Agricultural Chemists*, **53**: 575–578 (1970).

Annex 9, Table 1.   Analysis for phosphorus in the
quality control materials; overall best estimate ± SD
mg/kg dry matter (no. of measurements)

Reference material	Concentration	
	This study	Certified value
A-11	11 219 ± 80 (5)	9 100 ± 1020[a]
HM-1	1251 ± (5)	—

[a] 95% confidence interval.

Individual results for specimens of A-11 and HM-1 analysed during
the course of this study did not show any variations outside the
expected range. As far as can be judged, therefore, the analytical
method provided reliable data throughout the course of the study.

Summary of values for concentrations of 24 elements in the quality control materials used in this study

Annex 10, Table 1 summarizes values for the 24 elements found for the two milk powder reference materials used in this study, cow's milk powder A-11 and human milk powder HM-1. The corresponding certified values for A-11 are also quoted where available.

For further discussion of the quality control aspects of this study, particularly for those elements for which recommended values are not yet available, see the relevant Annexes.

Annex 10, Table 1. Summary of values for concentrations of 24 elements in the milk quality control materials used in this study, overall best estimate ± SD in mg/kg dry weight (no. of measurements). Further discussion can be found in the Annex indicated

Element	A-11			HM-1	
	This study	Certified value[a]	Recent inter-comparison data[b]	This study	Annex
Antimony				0.011 ± 42% (29)	5
Arsenic	0.0048 ± 4% (8)		0.00485 ± 4% (4)	0.0013 ± 23% (12)	7
Cadmium	< 0.01		0.0017 ± 12% (3)	< 0.006	4
Calcium	13 110 ± 10% (6)	12 900 ± 6.2%		2 290 ± 3.7% (5)	3
Chlorine	9 920 ± 2.9% (8)	9 080 ± 19%		2 748 ± 3.9% (19)	4
Chromium	0.018 ± 30% (6)		0.0177 ± 21% (6)	0.009 ± 60% (8)	3
Cobalt	0.0051 ± 21% (19)		0.0045 ± 18% (6)	0.0015 ± 47% (29)	5
Copper	0.39 ± 6% (19)	0.84 ± 20%[c]	0.378 ± 8% (9)	1.6 ± 8.5% (29)	5
Fluorine	0.176 ± 13% (24)			0.054 ± 13% (14)	8
Iodine	0.090 ± 6% (4)	3.65 ± 21%[d]	0.87 ± 7% (3)	0.32 ± 8% (21)	7
Iron	2.24 ± 21% (19)			1.95 ± 29% (29)	5
Lead			0.054 ± 19% (3)	0.09 ± 32% (24)	6
Magnesium	1 130 ± 5% (6)	1 100 ± 7.3%		257 ± 2.6% (6)	3
Manganese	0.26 ± 9% (19)	0.38 ± 21%[c]	0.257 ± 2% (3)	0.072 ± 9.8% (29)	5
Mercury		0.0025 ± 28%	0.0032 ± 19% (4)	0.008 ± 43% (29)	5

Molybdenum	0.085 ± 11% (6)			0.007 ± 50% (4)	4
Nickel		0.092 ± 10% (5)		0.11 ± 28% (24)	6
Phosphorus	11 219 ± 0.7% (5)		9 100 ± 11%	1 251 ± 1.7% (5)	9
Potassium	17 600 ± 10% (6)		17 200 ± 5.8%	3 841 ± 3.5% (6)	3
Sodium	4 100 ± 10% (6)		4 420 ± 7.5%	822 ± 4.0% (6)	3
Selenium	0.031 ± 13% (5)		0.034 ± 21%	0.074 ± 9% (21)	5
Tin					7
Vanadium	0.00092 ± 11% (7)			0.0006 ± 25% (16)	7
Zinc	34.7 ± 8% (16)		38.9 ± 5.9%	12.1 ± 7.4% (21)	5

[a] Recommended concentration (see page 8) with 95% confidence interval.
[b] From: Byrne, A. R. et al. *Fresenius Zeitung zur analytische Chemie*, 326: 723-729 (1987).
[c] Probably erroneously high (see Annex 5).
[d] There is some doubt about this value (see Annex 5).

WHO publications may be obtained, direct or through booksellers, from:

ALGERIA: Entreprise nationale du Livre (ENAL), 3 bd Zirout Youcef, ALGIERS

ARGENTINA: Carlos Hirsch, SRL, Florida 165, Galerías Güemes, Escritorio 453/465, BUENOS AIRES

AUSTRALIA: Hunter Publications, 58A Gipps Street, COLLINGWOOD, VIC 3066.

AUSTRIA: Gerold & Co., Graben 31, 1011 VIENNA I

BAHRAIN: United Schools International, Arab Region Office, P.O. Box 726, BAHRAIN

BANGLADESH: The WHO Representative, G.P.O. Box 250, DHAKA 5

BELGIUM: *For books:* Office International de Librairie s.a., avenue Marnix 30, 1050 BRUSSELS. *For periodicals and subscriptions:* Office International des Périodiques, avenue Louise 485, 1050 BRUSSELS.

BHUTAN: *see* India, WHO Regional Office

BOTSWANA: Botsalo Books (Pty) Ltd., P.O. Box 1532, GABORONE

BRAZIL: Centro Latinoamericano de Informação em Ciencias de Saúde (BIREME), Organização Panamericana de Saúde, Sector de Publicações, C.P. 20381.- Rua Botucatu 862, 04023 SÃO PAULO, SP

BURMA: *see* India, WHO Regional Office

CAMEROON: Cameroon Book Centre, P.O. Box 123, South West Province, VICTORIA

CANADA: Canadian Public Health Association, 1565 Carling Avenue, Suite 400, OTTAWA, Ont. K1Z 8R1. (Tel: (613) 725–3769. Telex: 21–053–3841)

CHINA: China National Publications Import & Export Corporation, P.O. Box 88, BEIJING (PEKING)

DEMOCRATIC PEOPLE'S REPUBLIC OF KOREA: *see* India, WHO Regional Office

DENMARK: Munksgaard Book and Subscription Service, P.O. Box 2148, 1610 COPENHAGEN K (Tel: + 45 1 12 85 70)

FIJI: The WHO Representative, P.O. Box 113, SUVA

FINLAND: Akateeminen Kirjakauppa, Keskuskatu 2, 00101 HELSINKI 10

FRANCE: Arnette, 2 rue Casimir-Delavigne, 75006 PARIS

GERMAN DEMOCRATIC REPUBLIC: Buchhaus Leipzig, Postfach 140, 701 LEIPZIG

GERMANY FEDERAL REPUBLIC OF: Govi-Verlag GmbH, Ginnheimerstrasse 20, Postfach 5360, 6236 ESCHBORN — Buchhandlung Alexander Horn, Kirchgasse 22, Postfach 3340, 6200 WIESBADEN

GREECE: G.C. Eleftheroudakis S.A., Librairie internationale, rue Nikis 4, 105-63 ATHENS

HONG KONG: Hong Kong Government Information Services, Publication (Sales) Office, Information Services Department, No. 1, Battery Path, Central, HONG KONG.

HUNGARY: Kultura, P.O.B. 149, BUDAPEST 62

ICELAND: Snaebjorn Jonsson & Co., Hafnarstraeti 9, P.O. Box 1131, IS-101 REYKJAVIK

INDIA: WHO Regional Office for South-East Asia, World Health House, Indraprastha Estate, Mahatma Gandhi Road, NEW DELHI 110002

IRAN (ISLAMIC REPUBLIC OF): Iran University Press, 85 Park Avenue, P.O. Box 54/551, TEHRAN

IRELAND: TDC Publishers, 12 North Frederick Street, DUBLIN 1 (Tel: 744835–749677)

ISRAEL: Heiliger & Co., 3 Nathan Strauss Street, JERUSALEM 94227

ITALY: Edizioni Minerva Medica, Corso Bramante 83–85, 10126 TURIN: Via Lamarmora 3, 20100 MILAN; Via Spallanzani 9, 00161 ROME

JAPAN: Maruzen Co. Ltd., P.O. Box 5050, TOKYO International, 100–31

JORDAN: Jordan Book Centre Co. Ltd., University Street, P.O. Box 301 (Al-Jubeiha), AMMAN

KENYA: Text Book Centre Ltd, P.O. Box 47540, NAIROBI

KUWAIT: The Kuwait Bookshops Co. Ltd., Thunayan Al-Ghanem Bldg, P.O. Box 2942, KUWAIT

LAO PEOPLE'S DEMOCRATIC REPUBLIC: The WHO Representative, P.O. Box 343, VIENTIANE

LUXEMBOURG: Librairie du Centre, 49 bd Royal, LUXEMBOURG

WHO publications may be obtained, direct or through booksellers, from:

MALAYSIA: The WHO Representative, Room 1004, 10th Floor, Wisma Lim Foo Yong (formerly Fitzpatrick's Building), Jalan Raja Chulan, KUALA LUMPUR 05–10; P.O. Box 2550, KUALA LUMPUR 01–02; Parry's Book Center, 124–1 Jalan Tun Sambanthan, P.O. Box 10960, 50730 KUALA LUMPUR

MALDIVES: *see* India, WHO Regional Office

MEXICO: Librería Interacademica S.A., Av. Sonora 206, 06100-MÉXICO, D.F.

MONGOLIA: *see* India, WHO Regional Office

MOROCCO: Editions La Porte, 281 avenue Mohammed V, RABAT

NEPAL: *see* India, WHO Regional Office

NETHERLANDS: InOr-Publikaties, P.O. Box 14, 7240 BA LOCHEM

NEW ZEALAND: New Zealand Government Printing Office, Publishing Administration, Private Bag, WELLINGTON; Walter Street, WELLINGTON; World Trade Building, Cubacade, Cuba Street, WELLINGTON. *Government Bookshops at:* Hannaford Burton Building, Rutland Street, Private Bag, AUCKLAND; 159 Hereford Street, Private Bag, CHRISTCHURCH; Alexandra Street, P.O. Box 857, HAMILTON; T & G Building, Princes Street, P.O. Box 1104, DUNEDIN — R. Hill & Son Ltd, Ideal House, Cnr Gillies Avenue & Eden Street, Newmarket, AUCKLAND 1

NORWAY: Tanum — Karl Johan A.S., P.O. Box 1177, Sentrum, N-0107 OSLO 1

PAKISTAN: Mirza Book Agency, 65 Shahrah–E–Quaid–E–Azam, P.O. Box 729, LAHORE 3

PAPUA NEW GUINEA: The WHO Representative, P.O. Box 646, KONEDOBU

PHILIPPINES: World Health Organization, Regional Office for the Western Pacific, P.O. Box 2932, MANILA; National Book Store Inc., 701 Rizal Avenue, P.O. Box 1934, MANILA

PORTUGAL: Livraria Rodrigues, 186 Rua do Ouro, LISBON 2

REPUBLIC OF KOREA: The WHO Representative, Central P.O. Box 540, SEOUL

SAUDI ARABIA: World of Knowledge for Publishing and Distribution, P.O. Box 576, JEDDAH

SINGAPORE: The WHO Representative, 144 Moulmein Road, SINGAPORE 1130; Newton P.O. Box 31, SINGAPORE 9122

SOUTH AFRICA: *Contact major book stores*

SPAIN: Comercial Atheneum S.A., Consejo de Ciento 130–136, 08015 BARCELONA; General Moscardó 29, MADRID 20 — Librería Díaz de Santos, P.O. Box 6050, 28006 MADRID; Balmes 417 y 419, 08022 BARCELONA

SRI LANKA: *see* India, WHO Regional Office

SWEDEN: *For books:* Aktiebolaget C.E. Fritzes Kungl. Hovbokhandel, Regeringsgatan 12, 103 27 STOCKHOLM. *For periodicals:* Wennergren-Williams AB, Box 30004, 104 25 STOCKHOLM

SWITZERLAND: Medizinischer Verlag Hans Huber, Länggassstrasse 76, 3012 BERN 9

THAILAND: *see* India, WHO Regional Office

UNITED KINGDOM: H.M. Stationery Office: 49 High Holborn, LONDON WC1V 6HB; 71 Lothian Road, EDINBURGH EH3 9AZ; 80 Chichester Street, BELFAST BT1 4JY; Brazennose Street, MANCHESTER M60 8AS; 258 Broad Street, BIRMINGHAM B1 2HE; Southey House, Wine Street, BRISTOL BS1 2BQ. *All mail orders should be sent to:* HMSO Publications Centre, 51 Nine Elms Lane, LONDON SW8 5DR

UNITED STATES OF AMERICA: *Copies of individual publications (not subscriptions):* WHO Publications Center USA, 49 Sheridan Avenue, ALBANY, NY 12210. *Subscription orders and correspondence concerning subscriptions should be addressed to the* World Health Organization, Distribution and Sales, 1211 GENEVA 27, Switzerland. *Publications are also available from the* United Nations Bookshop, NEW YORK, NY 10017 (*retail only*)

USSR: *For readers in the USSR requiring Russian editions:* Komsomolskij prospekt 18, Medicinskaja Kniga, MOSCOW — *For readers outside the USSR requiring Russian editions:* Kuzneckij most 18, Meždunarodnaja Kniga, MOSCOW G-200

VENEZUELA: Librería Medica Paris, Apartado 60.681, CARACAS 106

YUGOSLAVIA: Jugoslovenska Knjiga, Terazije 27/II, 11000 BELGRADE

ZIMBABWE: Textbook Sales (PVT) Ltd, 1 Norwich Union Centre, MUTARE

Special terms for developing countries are obtainable on application to the WHO Representatives or WHO Regional Offices listed above or to the World Health Organization, Distribution and Sales Service, 1211 Geneva 27, Switzerland. Orders from countries where sales agents have not yet been appointed may also be sent to the Geneva address, but must be paid for in pounds sterling, US dollars, or Swiss francs. Unesco book coupons may also be used.

Prices are subject to change without notice.